Excel

Year 4 NAPLAN*-style Tests

Alan Horsfield & Allyn Jones

PASCAL
PRESS

The authors wish to thank James Athanasou and Angella Deftereos for permission to use their Introduction.

ISBN 978 1 74125 387 0

Pascal Press
PO Box 250
Glebe NSW 2037
(02) 9557 4844
www.pascalpress.com.au

Publisher: Vivienne Joannou
Project Editor: Mark Dixon
Edited by Rosemary Peers
Proofread and answers checked by Peter Little and Dale Little
Cover, page design and typesetting by DiZign Pty Ltd
Printed by Green Giant Press

CONTENTS

INTRODUCTION

This book is designed for students preparing for their NAPLAN Tests, parents who want to help their children and teachers who wish to prepare their class for the NAPLAN Tests. Students may also use these books separately from the tests and parents as a general way of revising or when tutoring their children.

Please note that there is no Year 4 NAPLAN Test. There are only Year 3 and Year 5 NAPLAN Tests. This book has been written to assist parents and teachers of Year 4 students in their preparation for the Year 5 NAPLAN Test.

We hope that you will find this guide easy to use and that it is useful in preparing students for these important tests. In the following sections we will try to answer some frequently asked questions about the tests.

What is NAPLAN?

NAPLAN stands for National Assessment Program—Literacy and Numeracy. It is the largest educational testing program in Australia.

The tests cover Reading, Writing, Language Conventions (Spelling, Grammar and Punctuation) and Numeracy. In other words, they cover what are known to many people as the basic skills of reading, writing and arithmetic.

What is the purpose of NAPLAN?

Although NAPLAN has been designed mainly to provide administrators and politicians with information about schools and educational systems, it is also relevant for each student. It provides a public record of his or her educational achievement.

It is amongst the most valuable series of tests that students will undertake in their primary and secondary schooling. Very often it will be their first formal public examination. There is no harm in preparing them for this event.

What is being assessed?

The content of the tests is based on what is generally taught across Australia, so don't be surprised if it doesn't match exactly what each student is learning in his or her class. Most schools should be teaching more than the basic levels of literacy and numeracy.

The tests cover only a specific range of skills. This is because literacy and numeracy are considered the basis for future learning in school. Of course, we recognise that there are many other personal or social skills that are important in life. We realise that students have their own special talents and aptitudes but at the same time governments want to be able to assess their educational achievement in some of the fundamental skills. It is important to emphasise that there are many different kinds of literacy and numeracy, and that these tests cover only some aspects.

What do the tests indicate?

The NAPLAN Tests are designed to be tests of educational achievement. They show what a student has learnt or can do.

They are not IQ tests. Students who do extremely well on these tests will be quite bright. It is possible, however, for some intelligent students to perform poorly because of disadvantage, language, illness or other factors.

Who does the NAPLAN Tests?

The NAPLAN Testing Program is held for students in Years 3, 5, 7 and 9 each year. The tests are designed for all students.

Some schools may exempt students from the tests. Those exempted may include students in special English classes, those who have recently arrived from non–English speaking backgrounds, or students with special disabilities.

Our advice to parents and guardians is that students should only undertake the test if it is likely to benefit them. It would be a pity if students were not personally or emotionally ready to perform at their best and the results underestimated their ability. The results on this occasion might label them inaccurately and it would be recorded in their confidential student record card. In some instances parents have insisted successfully that their child be exempt from the testing.

Who is developing these tests?

The tests were originally developed by the Curriculum Corporation in conjunction with State and Territory Departments of Education or Boards of Studies and are now being developed by ACARA (Australian Curriculum, Assessment and Reporting Authority). These are large-scale educational tests in which the questions are extensively trialled. Any poor questions should have been eliminated in these trials. The tests are designed to produce results with high validity and reliability.

How can the results be used?

The results of the NAPLAN Tests offer an opportunity to help students at an early stage of their schooling. The findings can be used as indicators of any problem areas.

It would be a pity to miss this chance to help students at this point in their schooling when it is still possible to address any issues. The findings can also be used as encouragement for students who are performing above the minimum standard.

It is important for parents and teachers to look closely at the student report. This indicates areas of strength and weakness. The report can

be a little complex to read at first but it contains quite a helpful summary of the skills assessed in Reading, Writing, Language Conventions and Numeracy. Use this as a guide for any revision.

If the NAPLAN Tests indicate that there are problems, repeated testing with other measures of educational achievement is strongly recommended. It is also relevant to compare the results of the NAPLAN Tests with general classroom performance.

Remember that all educational test results have limitations. Don't place too much faith in the results of a single assessment.

Does practice help?

There is no benefit in trying to teach to the NAPLAN Tests because they contain so many different questions and these will vary from year to year. Nevertheless, a general preparation for the content of the NAPLAN Tests should be quite helpful.

Practice will help students overcome unfamiliarity with test procedures and specific forms of questions. It should also help them perform to the best of their ability.

Use the tests in this book to practise test skills and also to diagnose some aspects of learning in Year 4. In saying this, parents should make sure that their child is keen and interested in undertaking these practice tests. There is no benefit in forcing students to practise.

Sometimes it is easy to forget that they are still young children. We recommend that you sit with them or at least stay nearby while they are completing each test. Give them plenty of praise and encouragement for their efforts.

How are students graded?

One of the big advantages of NAPLAN is that it uses a single scale of achievement. This has 10 levels of achievement that are called bands. It will then be possible for you to see how much progress has been made by each student in literacy and numeracy from Year 3 to Year 9. Normally we would expect students to increase their level of achievement at each stage. In this book we have tried to grade the questions into levels of difficulty for you.

Each year of NAPLAN covers different bands. These are shown in the table below.

Bands covered in Year 3	Bands covered in Year 5	Bands covered in Year 7	Bands covered in Year 9
			10
		9	9
	8	8	8
	7	7	7
6	6	6	6
5	5	5	5
4	4	4	
3	3		
2			
1			

How our book's grading system works

Step 1

In this book you will notice that we have provided *Check your skills* pages (please turn to page 30). These pages provide you with information about the approximate level of difficulty of each question in the *Practice tests* section. We have divided the questions into three levels of difficulty: Basic, Intermediate and Advanced.

Step 2

Once you have completed the checklists, you will be able to see at a glance your student's approximate level of ability. All you have to do is find the point where the student started having consistent difficulty with questions. For example, if he or she answers most questions correctly up to the Intermediate level and

then gets most questions wrong from then onwards, it is likely his or her ability is at an Intermediate level.

What results are provided for parents and teachers?

Parents, teachers and schools receive comprehensive test results. These enable interpretation of results at a personal and group level.

The parent reports will show performance in broad skill bands. Some people will look only at the band reached on these tests, but really it is more important to see what a student knows or can do.

The bands covering the middle 60% of students will be shaded in a lighter colour in the report provided to parents. This is called the average range, but really it is quite a large group. There is a huge difference between students at the top and bottom of this average range. Averages tend to hide more than they reveal. It will, however, be possible to see whether a student is performing above or below the expected range of performance.

Each band will list a student's skills in specific areas of literacy and numeracy. The results are not straightforward to interpret and some assistance may be required. The bands are not a percentage.

Nevertheless, check to see what each student knows or can do. See where he or she needs extra help. Look at his or her strengths in the fields of literacy and numeracy. Then check how the class or school performed and where the student is placed within the group as well as in comparison with all other students in their year group. Once again, a knowledge of how to interpret test results is required and you should seek assistance. The worst thing you can do is just to look superficially at the bands—it is important that these are used for the benefit of each student.

Are the tests in Year 3 and Year 5 the same?

The tests increase in difficulty but the general content is much the same. Some questions might be repeated. This is because it allows the test developers to standardise the results across Years 3 and 5. The similar questions act like anchors for all the other questions.

When are the tests held?

The tests are held in May on an agreed date. The actual timetable is listed on the official NAPLAN website (www.naplan.edu.au). They are spread over three days. The tests should be given in the mornings.

What are the types of questions?

Many questions are multiple choice but some require students to express their answers in different ways. There is also a writing component that is graded.

Some people think that the multiple-choice questions that are used in the tests disadvantage students. Others think that multiple choice can only assess trivial details. Some might think that students are able to pass multiple-choice tests by guessing. We don't agree with any of these assertions—it all depends on how well the questions are written, whether there are sufficient questions, whether they assess the relevant skills and whether they have been pilot tested on a preliminary group. In the absence of any other compelling reasons, multiple choice is by far the preferred option for large-scale testing.

Please note that multiple-choice tests are not influenced by guessing because the options should be written so that they are almost equally attractive. Someone who has the ability should immediately recognise the answer, whereas someone who does not have the ability would think that all the options

are possible. The chances are very low that someone could guess their way to a high score.

Furthermore, not everyone realises that in NAPLAN there are many questions in the tests that require short answers, as well as performance tests in the area of writing. In fact it would probably make little difference what format is used. By and large bright students will typically do well whatever the method of assessment and those students who are well below average will struggle with whatever method of assessment is used.

Overall, in our judgement the NAPLAN Tests appear to be of quite a high technical standard and we should have reasonable confidence in the results.

Are there time limits?

Yes, there are time limits for each test. These are usually set so that 95% of students can complete the tests in the time allowed.

If more than one test is scheduled on a day, there should be a reasonable rest break of at least 20 minutes between tests. In some special cases students may be given some extra time and allowed to complete a response.

Will students be shown what to do?

Our education systems now have considerable experience with large-scale testing. The testing program is normally very well organised with clear instructions given to schools and teachers. Teachers receive special instructions for administering the tests.

Teachers will probably give students practice tests in the weeks before the NAPLAN Tests. Students will be shown how to complete the information on the cover of the tests and how to show their answers.

If a student has special needs (such as requiring a writer or extra time), please check the day before that the appropriate arrangements have been made by the school.

Are copies of the tests available?

All tests are returned to the education department for marking. Sample questions and past papers are available on the official NAPLAN website (www.naplan.edu.au). Many schools and teachers may also have copies. Under no circumstances should students ever be allowed to practise on the real test as this destroys the validity and accuracy of the test results.

How is this book organised?

This book is divided into sample questions and practice tests. We start with samples of the Numeracy and Literacy (Reading and Language Conventions) questions. Work through these examples so that every student knows what needs to be done. At the very least, please ensure that each student is at least familiar with the sample questions.

This is then followed by four practice tests for Numeracy, four practice tests for Reading and four practice tests for Language Conventions. There are also six practice tests for Writing. At the very least, revise the sample questions if you do not have enough time to do the practice tests.

• • • • •

Please note that it isn't really possible to predict specifically what the content of the NAPLAN Tests might be. In our opinion the content seems to vary somewhat from the earlier Basic Skills Tests or Achievement Improvement Monitor (AIM) Tests. This could be because it focuses on 'the essential elements that should be taught at the appropriate year levels'. There is a greater use of pictorial supplementary material. Our initial impression is that the NAPLAN Tests are easier than their predecessors.

The questions in this book are only a guide. Check the official NAPLAN website for additional details and past papers. The reader is advised that there will be changes in format and content from year to year.

So welcome again to *Excel Year 4 NAPLAN*-style Tests*. Thank you for your patience in working through this introduction. We hope you find this guide helpful. It is designed to be easy to use and to help students prepare for the tests.

We are grateful for the editing of Rosemary Peers and would like to thank Peter Little and Dale Little for checking answers. In preparing this edition we would like to acknowledge the cooperation and support of the publishers Matthew Sandblom, Vivienne Joannou and Mark Dixon of Pascal Press. We wish every student well in the NAPLAN Tests and in their future studies.

Introduction

The *My School* website (www.myschool.edu.au) provides the NAPLAN results for around 10 000 Australian schools. It has been a source of controversy because it allows everyone to see a school's overall results in the NAPLAN Tests. It will also allow comparison—fairly or unfairly—with other schools.

Each school has a profile page that includes a description of the school. It includes social background as well as educational data about the school, including the number of students and teachers, attendance rates, information about students' backgrounds and other details.

The school's NAPLAN results are compared with the national average and the average results of similar schools. Here is a sample of the results that you might see. It is taken from the page of one high school. This is a high-performing high school but one that doesn't prepare its students specifically for the tests through special practice.

2009	2008									
	Reading		Writing		Spelling		Grammar & Punctuation		Numeracy	
Year 3										
Year 5										
Year 7	652		628		657		674		709	
	SIM 594	ALL 541	SIM 577	ALL 532	SIM 577	ALL 540	SIM 594	ALL 539	SIM 601	ALL 544
Year 9	675		671		696		706		761	
	SIM 637	ALL 580	SIM 629	ALL 569	SIM 625	ALL 576	SIM 635	ALL 574	SIM 657	ALL 589

The chart displays the average NAPLAN scores for Reading, Writing, Spelling, Grammar and Punctuation, and Numeracy in 2009. The scores of the school are shown in the top row (in blue on the website). Beneath this—under the heading *SIM*—you will see the average scores for what are considered similar schools. Under the heading *ALL* you will see the results for all Australian schools. If the coloured bars are green, it indicates that the school's scores are above the other scores.

If the coloured bars are red, it means that the school is below the similar schools or below all other schools.

Common scale

For this school you can see that in each case the score was above that for similar schools and certainly well above that for all other high schools. If you take Reading, for example, you will see that the average score for this school was 652 in Year 7, compared with 594 for similar schools and 541 for all other schools. It is fairly likely that this is a selective school.

For each of the five NAPLAN areas (Reading, Writing, Spelling, Grammar and Punctuation, and Numeracy) there is a common scale. Each scale has an average score of 500. Around 68% of schools have average scores within the range of 400 to 600.

This school's score of 652 for Reading in Year 7 is above the average of 500 and in the top 16% throughout Australia (16% of schools score less than 400, 68% score from 400 to 600, and 16% score more than 600). Of course, this school did even better in Numeracy in Years 7 and 9.

Other pages

Other pages on the *My School* website show additional information, such as the percentage of students achieving at each band in the NAPLAN Tests.

• • • • •

Note that the *My School* website provides an overall indication of a school's performance but it does not say anything about individual students.

Test materials

All the test materials are contained in this book. There are answers for scoring the responses. There are also diagnostic charts to help you. The diagnostic charts are only an approximate guide to achievement bands.

Equipment

Students will not need rulers, white-out, pens or calculators. It is best to use a pencil. On the test day students should be provided with a pencil, an eraser and a blank sheet of paper for rough working.

Time limits

Try to keep roughly to the time limits for the practice tests. You may give some students extra time if they are tired. Even a short break every 20 minutes is appropriate.

Instructions to students

Explain patiently what needs to be done. Students should only attempt these practice tests if they wish to and do no more than one test in a session.

Recording answers

Show students the way to mark the answers. They have to colour in circles, shapes or numbers, or write the answers in the boxes or on the lines provided.

Numeracy Tests

The Numeracy Tests in this book have 35 to 40 questions. Allow around 45 minutes for Numeracy Tests 1 and 2, and 50 minutes for Numeracy Tests 3 and 4.

Try not to explain terms during the testing. This can be done after the practice session. If a question is still too hard, it is better to leave it at this stage. Some students may not be ready for the task. There is a diagnostic chart at the end of each Numeracy Test to help you identify any problem areas.

Literacy Tests

Literacy is divided into three tests: Reading, Language Conventions and Writing.

Allow around 50 minutes for Reading Tests, and 40 minutes for Language Conventions and Writing Tests, with a break in between. Don't explain terms during the testing. This can be done after the practice session.

The Writing Tests offer assistance with aspects of writing using prompts and stimulus materials.

- In the Reading Tests students will read stories and non-fiction writing. There will be supporting pictures and charts. Students will be asked to find information, make conclusions, find the meaning, or even look at different ideas.

- For the Writing Tests students will write specific text types. They will be judged on the structure of their writing, as well as their grammar, punctuation and spelling.

- The Language Conventions Tests are divided into two parts: spelling, and grammar and punctuation. Students will be asked to check words and also to correct words with less regular spelling. They must also be able to use verbs and punctuation, such as speech marks and commas, correctly.

The next section contains the sample questions for Numeracy, Reading and Language Conventions. After the sample questions there are 18 practice tests of the different aspects of literacy and numeracy.

SAMPLE QUESTIONS—NUMERACY

Here are some sample questions. Make sure you read each question carefully so that you know exactly:

- what information is given to you in the question
- what the question is asking you to find.

Then make sure you read each answer option carefully in order to choose the correct answer. You can use a calculator to help you answer these questions. There is no time limit for the sample questions.

If you aren't sure what to do, ask your teacher or your parents to help you. Don't be afraid to ask if it isn't clear to you.

To answer these questions, write the answer in the box or colour in the circle with the correct answer. Colour in only one circle for each answer.

---

1. What is the place value of the 6 in the number 3607?

   ○ 6 units   ○ 6 tens
   ● 6 hundreds   ○ 6 thousands

2. The length of a glue stick is closest to

   ● 10 cm   ○ 10 mm
   ○ 50 cm   ○ 100 cm

3. Sam uses this spinner.

   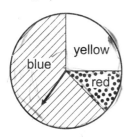

   Which colour is she most likely to spin?

   red   yellow   blue   green
   ○   ○   ✓   ○

4. School finishes at 3:10 pm.
   Which clock is showing this time?

   ○   ○   ○   ✓

5. Vallie wrote these number sentences on four cards.

   Which one equals 2090?

   ✓ | 2000 + 90 |

   ○ | 20 + 90 |

   ○ | 200 + 90 |

   ○ | 2000 + 9 |

6. For Easter, Jamie gave his mother a box containing 4 rows of 5 chocolates.

   What was the total number of chocolates in the box?

   9   12   18   20
   ○   ○   ○   ✓

7. Carmen wrote these numbers.

   | 1985 | 5998 | 7003 | 2094 |

   Which is the largest number?

   7003

   Write your answer in the box.

☞ Answers and explanations on page 6

8. 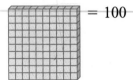 = 1   = 10 and

= 100

What number is shown?

 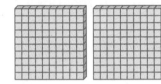

342	234	243	324
○	○	○	○

9. What is the area of the shaded shape, in square units?

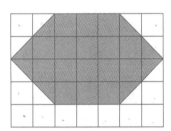

○ 12 square units   ○ 16 square units

○ 20 square units   ○ 24 square units

10. Bridgett asked 70 students at her school what their favourite pet was.

The table below shows her results.

	Dog	Cat	Bird	Fish	Total
Year 3	7	5	3	1	16
Year 4	6	4	6	4	20
Year 5	3	6	2	3	14
Year 6	8	7	3	2	20
Total	24	22	14	10	70

How many Year 4 students said their favourite pet was a cat?

Write your answer in the box.

11. Which of these numbers is closest to 1250?

126	1200	1260	1520
○	○	○	○

12. Which of these objects is made from 4 cubes?

○   ○   ○   ○

13. Here are some candles.

Which candle is in the shape of a cone?

○   ○   ○   ○

14. The graph shows the favourite colour chosen by students.

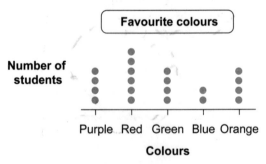

What was the total number of students who preferred red **or** blue?

4	7	8	9
○	○	○	○

15. Which of these has the same value as 6 × 5?

○ 4 × 7 + 3   ○ 8 × 4 − 3

○ 10 × 4 − 5   ○ 4 × 5 + 10

16.

How many more hearts can fit inside the rectangle?

8	10	12	16
○	○	○	○

17. Here is a 2-litre bottle of milk.

What is the best estimate of its mass?

○ 200 grams

○ 2000 grams

○ 20 grams

○ 2 grams

18.

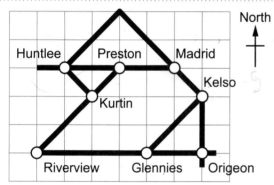

A map is drawn on a grid showing roads around the town of Preston.

Emilee left Preston and travelled East, then South-East and then South.

Which town has she arrived at?

○ Riverview

○ Glennies

○ Origeon

○ Kurtin

19. The shape in the left box is **flipped** over the dotted line to form a shape in the right box.

Which of these shows the new shape and the old shape?

○   ○   ○   ○

20.

3700	÷	?	=	37

What is the missing number?

 Write your answer in the box.

21. How many 4s are in 412?

 Write your answer in the box.

22. A farmer's hens lay 120 eggs each day.

The eggs are sold for $5 per dozen.

If the farmer sells all the eggs, how much will he earn each day?

$40	$50	$60	$170
○	○	○	○

23. A cyclist rode 120 kilometres in a weekend.

If he rode 20 kilometres more on Saturday than he did on Sunday, how many kilometres did he ride on Saturday?

 km Write your answer in the box.

24. Bags of 6 bread rolls sell for $3.00.

What is the most number of bread rolls that can be bought for $12.00?

24	12	72	18
○	○	○	○

☞ Answers and explanations on page 6

25. What is the perimeter of the shape?

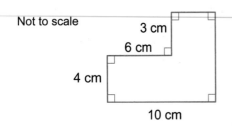

Not to scale
3 cm
6 cm
4 cm
10 cm

23 cm   27 cm   30 cm   34 cm
○   ○   ○   ○

26. Here is a number line.

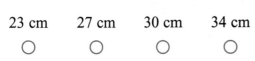

0   A   B $\frac{1}{2}$ C   1   D $1\frac{1}{2}$

Which letter is pointing to $\frac{3}{4}$?

A   B   C   D
○   ○   ○   ○

27. Taylah uses some of these cards to make an even number.

What is the largest number she can make between 300 and 3000?

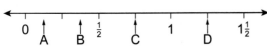

| 0 | 9 | 4 | 2 | 8 | 3 |

[ ]   **Write your answer in the box.**

28. A shop sells four brands of sunglasses.

$29.95 $39.95 $24.95 $44.95

What is the difference in price between the most expensive brand and the least expensive brand of sunglasses?

$ [ ]    **Write your answer in the box.**

29. In a bag there are 20 balls.

- The bag only contains red, green, blue and yellow balls.
- Six of the balls are red.
- There are half as many green balls as red balls.
- There are four more blue balls than green balls.

How many yellow balls are in the bag?

4   6   2   5
○   ○   ○   ○

30. Which of these is correct?

○ $6 \times 2 + 5 > 80 \div 4$

○ $46 - 12 < 8 \times 2$

○ $30 \div 10 + 4 < 6 + 19$

○ $12 + 32 > 48$

31. Every straight line in this puzzle contains three numbers which add to 90.

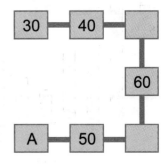

30	40	
		60
A	50	

What is the number that replaces the letter A?

10   30   40   70
○   ○   ○   ○

☞ Answers and explanations on page 6

32. Students in a class were asked to guess the height of a tomato plant growing in their school garden.

Luke's guess	Thomas's guess
120 cm	$1\frac{1}{2}$ metres

Brodie's guess	Loukia's guess
1400 mm	1.1 m

The class teacher measured the height to be 105 centimetres.

Which student had the closest guess?

Luke   Thomas   Brodie   Loukia
○   ○   ○   ○

33. The graph shows the number of people sitting in a doctor's waiting room throughout a day.

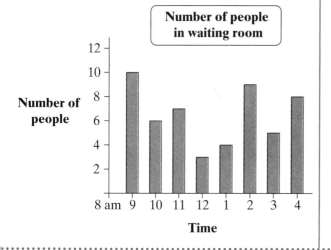

There are 14 chairs in the waiting room.

How many empty chairs were there at 3 pm?

5   11   9   14
○   ○   ○   ○

34. Here is a number chart.

David shades the multiples of 3.

1	2	3	4	5	6	7	8	9	10
11	12	13	14	15	16	17	18	19	20
21	22	23	24	25	26	27	28	29	30

Here is another section of the same chart.

51	52	53	54	54	56	57	58	59	60
61	62	63	64	65	66	67	68	69	70

If David continues the same number pattern, how many squares will he shade in this section of the chart?

6   7   8   9
○   ○   ○   ○

35. The netball canteen workers sell pies and sausage rolls.

For every 3 pies sold, the canteen sells 2 sausage rolls.

How many sausage rolls are sold if one Saturday the canteen sells 36 pies?

18   12   20   24
○   ○   ○   ○

END OF QUESTIONS

Well done! You have completed the sample questions for Numeracy. Even if you don't practise any others, at least you have some familiarity with the method used in the NAPLAN tests.

How did you go with these sample questions? Check to see where you did well and where you had problems. Try to revise the questions that were hard for you.

There are now four more Numeracy tests to practise, each containing 35 or 40 questions. They include many of the same types of questions, plus a few other types.

☞ Answers and explanations on page 6

ANSWERS TO SAMPLE QUESTIONS—NUMERACY

1. **6 hundreds.** The number is made up of 3 thousands, 6 hundreds, 0 tens and 7 ones.

2. **10 cm.** Know the lengths of familiar objects; for example, a ruler is 30 cm long. This helps you work out that a glue stick would be about 10 cm.

3. **blue.** The biggest part of the spinner is blue and so the arrow has a bigger chance of stopping there.

4. Ten past means the big hand is on the 2.

5. **2000 + 90.** The number 2090 says two thousand and ninety.

6. **20.** 4 rows of 5 means 4 times 5, or 4 × 5 which equals 20.

7. **7003.** This number is more than 7 thousand and is a lot more than any of the other numbers.

8. **243.** The picture shows 2 hundreds, 4 rows of 10 and 3 ones. This means 200 + 40 + 3 which is 243.

9. **20 square units.** First, count the squares, and then count the triangles because 2 triangles make a square. The 8 triangles can be counted as 4 squares and adding the other 16 squares means a total of 20 squares.

10. **4.** Look at the Year 4 row and the Cat column. The number is 4.

11. **1260.** This is the closest number because it is just 10 away from 1250.

12. 3 cubes can be seen and there is another cube that can't be seen.

13.

14. **8.** There are 6 dots for red and 2 dots for blue. Adding 6 and 2 gives 8.

15. **4 × 5 + 10.** First, 6 × 5 is 30. Now check all the choices and the only one that equals 30 is 4 × 5 + 10 because 20 + 10 is 30.

16. **12.** 2 more hearts will fit on the 2nd row, 4 on the 3rd row and 6 on the bottom row. Now add the numbers: 2 + 4 + 6 is 12.

17. **2000 grams.** The milk would have a mass of about 2 kilograms which is 2000 grams.

18. **Origeon.** She leaves Preston, passes through Madrid, then Kelso and then arrives at Origeon.

19. The dotted line in the middle is like a mirror.

20. **100.** The question is 37 hundred divided by a number is 37. This means the missing number is a hundred.

21. **103.** 412 ÷ 4 = 103. Make sure you put the 0 in. This is the way to work it out: 4 into 4 goes 1; then 4 into 1 won't go; then 4 into 12 goes 3. So the answer is 103.

22. **$50.** There are 12 in a dozen and so there are 10 dozen eggs. Then multiplying by 5 gives $50.

23. **70.** First halve the 120 which gives 60 and then halve the 20 which gives 10. This means he rode 10 more than 60 on Saturday and 10 less than 60 on Sunday. He rode 70 kilometres on Saturday.

24. **24.** As a bag costs $3 then 4 bags can be bought for $12. Now as there are 6 bread rolls in each bag, 4 lots of 6 is 24.

25. **34 cm.** The vertical sides of 4 and 3 add up to 7 and the horizontal sides add up to 10. Adding all the numbers gives 34.
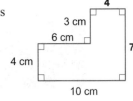

26. **C.** Between 0 and 1 the number line has been divided into quarters. As C is pointing to the 3rd, it is $\frac{3}{4}$.

27. **2984.** The largest number below 3000 will start with 2000. Then use the largest digits going downwards after that to get 2984.

28. **$20.** The difference is between $44.95 and $24.95 which is $20.

29. **4.** There are 6 red, 3 green and 7 blue balls. When these are added together you get 16 which means there must be 4 yellow balls.

30. **30 ÷ 10 + 4 < 6 + 19.** Work through each of the choices using > as greater than and < as less than. Here, 30 ÷ 10 + 4 is 3 + 4 = 7 which is less than 6 + 19 = 25.

31. **30.** Every straight line adds to 90. Working through each line from the top you find the puzzle looks like this:
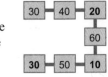

32. **Loukia.** Change all the guesses to centimetres. Luke (120), Thomas (150), Brodie (140) and Loukia (110). This means the closest is 110 cm.

33. **9.** At 3 pm there were 5 people sitting in the waiting room. As 14 minus 5 is 9, there were 9 empty chairs.

34. **7.** To make it easy start with 60 as it is a multiple of 3. Counting backwards in 3s from 60 will give you 4 boxes to be shaded on the top row and counting forwards from 60 will give you 3 boxes on the second row: 51, 54, 57, 60, 63, 66, 69.

35. **24.** Start with 3 pies and 2 sausage rolls. Now multiply these numbers by 12 to give you 36 pies and 24 sausage rolls.

SAMPLE QUESTIONS—READING

Here are some sample questions. For the reading questions you will need to look at a picture or read a text. Make sure you read each question carefully so that you know exactly what the question is asking. Then find the relevant section in the text. Finally make sure you read each answer option carefully in order to choose the correct answer. There is no time limit for the sample questions.

To answer these questions, write the answer on the line or lines or colour in the circle which has the right answer. Colour in only one circle for each answer.

If you aren't sure what to do, ask your teacher or your parents to help you. Don't be afraid to ask if it isn't clear to you.

Read the text about *Uncle Fred* and answer questions 1 to 7.

In the back street was a skip bin of building rubble. Beside a front-end loader, on the footpath was a mess of old kitchen cupboards, ready to be carted to the tip.

5 Uncle Fred was impressed. Doors with handles, cupboards and pieces of timber. Uncle Fred hurried off for his toolbox.

Before long, Uncle Fred was knocking the old cupboards apart and collecting sheets of
10 chipboard and lengths of timber.

'I'll show them,' he said to Buster. 'My own "after-life container", for when I go upstairs.' Buster found that odd. They didn't have stairs in their home.

15 Uncle Fred began making a strange long box. Buster was allowed to help. Soon they were sawing, hammering—and humming away.

They added a lid, using hinges from a pantry door and catches from a kitchen cupboard.

20 'It'll make a great "resting place",' said Uncle Fred. 'Might as well be comfortable when I kick the bucket.'

Make a better hiding place, thought Buster. Then he wondered why Uncle Fred was
25 going to kick a bucket.

'We could put a little window in it,' suggested Buster with a smile.

Uncle Fred gave him an odd look.

'So you can watch TV while you are
30 resting,' explained Buster, feeling confused.

'Better for watching worms when I'm pushing up daisies! Anyway, needs padding,' said Uncle Fred and ambled off, whistling.

Buster thought that if Uncle Fred was going
35 to rest in it he'd need air. He didn't know anything about growing daisies. He drilled large holes in the lid making an F for Fred.

Buster decided to see how he'd fit. He lay down in the box. It was a bit long, but it
40 was wide enough.

He pulled the lid over. *Click. Click!* The holes were in the right places. He could see bits of sky. Then he tried to push the lid open. It was stuck! The catches had clicked
45 into place.

1. Where was the skip bin?
   - ○ upstairs in Buster's house
   - ○ near the daisy garden
   - ○ in the kitchen
   - ✓ in the back street

2. What was Uncle Fred making?
   - ○ kitchen cupboards
   - ○ a flower garden
   - ✓ a coffin
   - ○ windows

3. Why did Buster drill holes in the lid?
   - ○ to let the light in
   - ✓ to let fresh air into the box
   - ✓ to make an F for Fred
   - ○ to make it possible for Uncle Fred to watch TV

4. Which word indicates that Uncle Fred was happy while working?
   - ○ humming
   - ○ comfortable
   - ✓ impressed
   - ○ ambled

5. Uncle Fred says he will *go upstairs*. What does he mean by this?
   - ✓ He has done enough work for one day.
   - ○ He has forgotten to get his tools.
   - ○ He will be going to Heaven when he dies.
   - ○ He is feeling confused.

6. How did Buster make the letter F?
   Write your answer on the line.

   He brilled

7. Choose the best title for the passage.
   - ○ The skip bin
   - ○ Back street rubbish
   - ○ Buster to the rescue
   - ○ Uncle Fred's project

Read *Cats sleep* and answer questions 8 to 11.

Cats sleep

Cats sleep, anywhere,
Any table, any chair
Top of piano, window-ledge,
In the middle, on the edge,
5 Open drawer, empty shoe,
Anybody's lap will do,
Fitted in a cardboard box,
In the cupboard, with your frocks—
Anywhere! They don't care!
10 Cats sleep anywhere.

Eleanor Farjeon (February 1881–1965)

8. Which statement describes the sleeping behaviour of cats.
   - ○ Cats are not fussy about where they sleep.
   - ○ Cats are very careful about where they sleep.
   - ○ Cats have favourite sleeping places.
   - ○ Cats are nervous about their sleeping places.

☞ Answers and explanations on page 14

9. Choose a word from the poem that rhymes with *frocks*.

Write your answer on the line.

_____

10. How does the poet feel about the sleeping habits of cats?

○ She is annoyed.

○ She is nervous.

○ She is surprised.

○ She is excited.

11. When Eleanor Farjeon wrote this poem she was pretending to talk to a

○ boy.

○ girl.

○ cat.

○ husband.

Read *Lake Eyre* and answer questions 12 to 17.

Lake Eyre

The lake was named after Edward John Eyre who was the first European to see it in 1840. It is in the deserts of South Australia. There is rarely much water in the lake even though many long rivers feed into it. Most of the rivers are often little more than a series of waterholes across thousands of kilometres of desert. In most dry seasons there is usually water in some of the shallow dips. The lowest part of the lake bed is 50 metres below sea level.

Lake Eyre lies in a wilderness surrounded by sand dunes. It is 144 kilometres long and 77 kilometres wide. Mostly the lake is a massive saltpan and water found there is undrinkable.

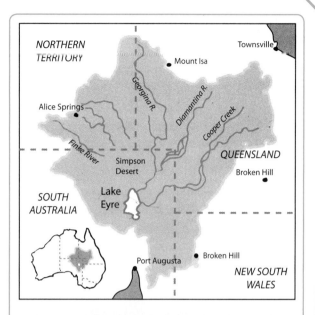

Lake Eyre has one of the largest areas of **inland drainage** in the world. During the rainy season the rivers from the north flow towards the lake through outback Queensland and the Northern Territory. Not all water reaches the lake. It can take months to get there—if it gets there at all.

Much of the water evaporates, or it soaks into the ground long before flowing into the lake. Heavy rain in January 2007 took six weeks to reach the lake but only a small amount of the water flowed into the lake.

Since 1885 the lake has filled about eight times, with the highest measurement being a flood of 6 metres in 1974. Local rain can sometimes fill Lake Eyre to 4 metres as occurred in both 1984 and 1989.

When the lake floods, it becomes a breeding site for large numbers of migratory waterbirds, How the birds know this remote lake is full no one knows.

12. This passage could be best described as

○ a scientific description.

○ an explanation.

◉ an information report.

○ a tourist's recount.

☞ Answers and explanations on page 14

13. The term *inland drainage* is used in the passage. *Inland drainage* refers to

- ● rivers that do not flow into the sea.
- ○ watercourses that are more like drains than rivers.
- ○ rivers that flows through deserts.
- ○ lakes that fill up on rare occasions.

14. What is one of the fascinating mysteries of Lake Eyre?

- ○ why the water cannot be drunk
- ○ the speed of water flowing into the lake
- ○ why the lake is so large
- ● how birds know there is water in the lake

15. The main purpose of the map is to show

- ○ how to get to the lake.
- ○ parts of South Australia that are desert.
- ● the area of land drained by the rivers.
- ○ why Lake Eyre got its name.

16. Most travellers to Lake Eyre could expect to see

- ○ birds.
- ● a saltpan.
- ○ flood waters.
- ○ heavy rain.

17. Leaving Lake Eyre and following Coopers Creek a traveller would pass through

- ● South Australia, then into Queensland.
- ○ Queensland, into South Australia.
- ○ South Australia, Queensland and then the Northern Territory.
- ○ South Australia, then into the Northern Territory.

Read *How to tie a reef knot* and answer questions 18 to 23.

How to tie a reef knot

A reef knot is also known as a square knot. It is a simple knot and can be used in many everyday situations. It is quick and easy to make and reliable, if not put under too
5 much strain. It is an ancient binding knot used to secure a rope or line around an object. It is used successfully in activities such as macramé (fancy lacework) and jewellery making.

10 Although the reef knot is often used for tying two lines together, it is not satisfactory for this due to its instability.

Steps

1. Start with two pieces
15   of string that are about the same thickness.
2. Make an 'X' with left over right, and both
20   ends pointing down.
3. Bring both ends upwards.
4. Turn the top right (dark colour) to
25   the left.
5. With your left hand, turn the light string into the loop and out again.
30   Pull tightly with both hands to form a symmetrical reef knot.

18. The reason for calling a reef knot a square knot is because of its

- ○ size.
- ○ strength.
- ○ speed of tying.
- ● shape.

10

19. A reef knot would be most useful for

- ○ hobbies.
- ○ post office work.
- ○ fishing and boating pursuits.
- ○ lifting activities.

20. Why are the two pieces of string used in the instructions different colours?

- ○ to make the diagrams attractive
- ○ to ensure people use two different bits of string
- ○ to make the instructions simple to follow
- ○ to fill the left-over space

21. This information would most likely be found in

- ○ a shopping catalogue.
- ○ a craft magazine.
- ○ an instruction manual.
- ○ the news section of a newspaper.

22. The reef knot is *reliable, if not put under too much strain.*

This suggests that users should not

- ○ pull too tightly on the knot.
- ○ put the knot near the end of the string.
- ○ use string that is old or damaged.
- ○ make the knot when feeling rushed.

23. Reef knots are useful for *everyday situations.*

Which of these would be an *everyday situation*?

- ○ climbing Mt Everest
- ○ bungy jumping
- ○ tying your shoelaces
- ○ fishing for sharks

Read the play script and answer questions 24 to 30.

Play script

SCENE: *This play is set in the dimly lit bedroom of two brothers. Ryan is snuggled up in his bed, almost asleep. A book lies half open on the bed. Shaun, the younger*
5 *brother, is in a low, hunched, sitting-up position on his bed, hugging his legs.*

Shaun:	You awake Ryan?
Ryan:	Uhh? What?
Shaun:	Guess what?
10 Ryan:	Shaun, I was nearly asleep!
Shaun:	You know what?
Ryan:	What, Shaun?
Shaun:	There's something under my bed. Something really big. It was there last night too. I think it is a … bunyip.
Ryan:	What? A bunyip? They're not real.
Shaun:	Are so. I felt it pushing up on the mattress. I was so scared I was hardly game to move. Or breathe.
Ryan:	What happened then?
Shaun:	I went to sleep. It was gone when I woke up.
25 Ryan:	It was a dream. Now let me go to sleep.
Shaun:	It was not a dream! I heard it too. It made soft grunting sounds. Like it was hungry. It was waiting for me to go to sleep so it could come out and eat me.

☞ **Answers and explanations on pages 14–15**

Ryan:	So why didn't it?
Shaun:	It must have forgotten. Maybe it thought I was still awake!
35 Ryan:	Maybe *it* went to sleep, waiting for you to go to sleep.
Shaun:	But I think its head poked up at the end of my bed before I went to sleep.
40 Ryan:	I'm going to sleep. Listen! Zzzzz. Zzzzz.
Shaun:	I remember now. I knew I was awake and, and …
Ryan:	And what?
45 Shaun:	It got under your bed! It's probably there now.
Ryan:	Good! That means I can prove how stupid you are!

Ryan sits up and drops his feet onto the
50 floor. Slowly he lifts the overhanging sheets
and peers under his bed. Shaun watches,
horrified.

Shaun:	Ryan stop! He'll get really mad.

Ryan gasps loudly.

55 Shaun:	What is it Ryan? What's there? It's the bunyip!
Ryan:	(*laughing*) No, it's a huge crocodile! Now, let me go back to sleep.

24. Which word would best describe Shaun?

○ timid

○ cheerful

○ daring

○ considerate

25. When Ryan is told about the creature under the bed he is

○ afraid.

○ disbelieving.

○ thoughtful.

○ understanding.

26. What was the main reason Shaun had for saying something was under his bed?

○ He heard it eating under his bed.

○ He saw its head near his feet.

○ He felt it pushing up on his mattress.

○ He could hear something moving from one bed to the other.

27. Why did Ryan make *Zzzzz* sounds?

○ He was asleep and snoring.

○ He wanted Shaun to stop asking questions.

○ He was listening for noises under the bed.

○ He was having trouble breathing.

28. Write the numbers 1 to 4 in the boxes to show the order of the following events in this text.

☐ Shaun warns Ryan about the monster under his bed.

☐ Ryan reads a book.

☐ Ryan gasps.

☐ Shaun makes sure Ryan is not asleep.

29. Why did Ryan gasp?

○ He saw a bunyip.

○ He realised that Shaun was telling the truth.

○ He wanted to give Shaun a fright.

○ He was looking at a crocodile.

30. The play script suggests that Shaun

○ had a vivid imagination.

○ was afraid of his brother.

○ never went to sleep.

○ didn't like reading.

Look at the cartoon and answer questions 31 to 35.

Cartoon

Cartoons are made up of frames. This one has four.

31. The reaction of the seagulls suggests that they are

○ frightened by the ship.

○ thrilled by the unexpected event.

○ disgusted by the actions of humans.

○ unable to understand what is happening.

32. A suitable caption for the cartoon would be:

○ The garbage collector

○ Peace in paradise

○ The rescue party

○ False alarm

33. In Frame 2 the man is most likely

○ trying to attract attention.

○ giving directions.

○ warning the ship of dangers.

○ swearing at the polluters.

34. How is the man feeling in Frame 4?

○ relieved

○ startled

○ dismayed

○ neglected

35. This cartoon has a serious message. What is that message?

○ Don't ignore stranded people.

○ We should help people in difficulty.

○ The oceans aren't giant rubbish dumps.

○ Life on a palm island is difficult.

END OF QUESTIONS

Well done! You have completed the sample questions for Reading. Even if you don't practise any other Reading Tests, at least you will have some familiarity with the method used in the NAPLAN Tests.

How did you go with these sample questions? Check to see where you did well and where you had problems. Try to revise the questions that were hard for you.

There are four more Reading Tests, each containing around 35 questions. They include many of the same types of questions, plus a few other types.

The spelling, grammar and punctuation questions are in the Language Conventions sample test. You can do this test now or you can leave it until later. Now take a break before you start any more tests.

☞ Answers and explanations on page 15

ANSWERS TO SAMPLE QUESTIONS—READING

1. **in the back street**. This is a **fact-finding type of question**. The answer is a fact in the text. You read that *In the back street was a skip bin of building rubble* (**see lines 1–2**).

2. **a coffin.** This is a **language type of question**. To find the answer you have to read the text carefully, especially where Uncle Fred calls what he is working on his '*own "after-life container"*' (**see line 12**). *After-life* refers to death. A coffin is a *container*.

3. **to let fresh air into the box.** This is a **fact-finding type of question**. The answer is a fact in the text. You read that *Buster thought that if Uncle Fred was going to rest in it he'd need air* (**see lines 34–35**).

4. **humming.** This is an **inferring type of question**. To find the answer you have to 'read between the lines'. You read *Soon they were sawing, hammering—and humming away* (**see lines 16–17**). Combine this information with your own knowledge of how people behave when they are happy and contented and you can work out that humming means Uncle Fred is happy.

5. **He will be going to Heaven when he dies.** This is a **language type of question**. To find the answer you have to read the text carefully, especially the section that is quoted: '*My own "after-life container", for when I go upstairs*' (**see lines 11–13**). *Going upstairs* is a saying people use when they don't want to use the words *death* or *die*.

6. **He used a drill.** This is a **fact-finding type of question**. The answer is a fact in the text. You read that Buster *drilled large holes in the lid making an F for Fred* (**see lines 36–37**).

7. **Uncle Fred's project.** This is a **synthesis type of question**. To find the answer you have to read the whole text. The text is about Uncle Fred making a coffin out of scrapped kitchen cupboards. The other options are minor details.

8. **Cats are not fussy about where they sleep.** This is an **inferring type of question**. To find the answer you have to 'read between the lines'. You read *Cats sleep, anywhere* (**see line 1**). A number of places where cats sleep are listed. Combine this information with your own knowledge of the meaning of *fussy* (concerned with minor details) to work out that cats are not fussy about where they sleep.

9. **box.** This is a **language type of question**. To find the answer you have to read the text carefully, especially Poems often have rhyming words at the end of lines. Words that rhyme do not have to have the same letter combination, e.g. *four* and *saw*.

10. **She is surprised.** This is an **inferring type of question**. To find the answer you have to 'read between the lines'. You read that cats sleep *Anywhere! They don't care!* (**see line 9**). The exclamation marks are an indication that the poet is mildly surprised.

11. **girl.** This is a **fact-finding type of question**. The answer is a fact in the text. You read that cats sleep *In the cupboard, with your frocks* (**see line 8**). Frocks (dresses) are worn by girls.

12. **an information report.** This is a **synthesis type of question**. To find the answer you have to read the whole text. The text provides information about Lake Eyre.

13. **rivers that do not flow into the sea.** This is a **fact-finding type of question**. The answer is a fact in the map. The map shows the reader that the rivers of the inland drainage system do not flow into the sea.

14. **how birds know there is water in the lake.** This is a **fact-finding type of question**. The answer is a fact in the text. You read that *How the birds know this remote lake is full no one knows* (**see lines 36–37**).

15. **the area of land drained by the rivers.** This is a **fact-finding type of question**. The answer is a fact on the map. The combined maps show the reader the vast area drained by the rivers.

16. **a saltpan.** This is an **inferring type of question**. To find the answer you have to 'read between the lines'. You read *Since 1885 the lake has filled about eight times* (**see lines 29–30**) and *Mostly the lake is a massive saltpan* (**see lines 14–15**). As the lake has only been full eight times in 125 years a tourist would be unlikely to see either flood waters or heavy rain. As birds only come when the lake is full a tourist would be unlikely see birds.

17. **South Australia, then into Queensland.** This is a **fact-finding type of question**. The answer is a fact on the map. The map shows the reader that Coopers Creek begins in Queensland and flows through South Australia to Lake Eyre.

18. **shape.** This is a **fact-finding type of question**. The answer is a fact in the final picture. The shape of the knot is somewhat like a rough square or rectangle.

19. **hobbies.** This is a **fact-finding type of question**. The answer is a fact in the text. You read that a reef knot *is used successfully in activities such as macramé (fancy lacework) and jewellery making* (**see lines 7–9**). These are hobbies which don't require too much strain.

20. **to make the instructions simple to follow.** This is an **inferring type of question**. To find the answer you have to 'read between the lines'. To find the answer you have to look at how the pictures line up with the steps to show what the instructions mean.

21. **a craft magazine** This is an **inferring type of question**. To find the answer you have to 'read between the lines'. You read that a reef knot *is used successfully in activities such as macramé (fancy lacework) and jewellery making* (see lines 7–9). These are hobbies or craft activities.

22. **pull too tightly on the knot.** This is a **language type of question**. To find the answer you have to read the text carefully, especially the section that is quoted: *It is quick and easy to make and reliable, if not put under too much strain* (see lines 3–5). *Strain* means 'draw tight or stretch' so one should not stretch the knot or pull it too tightly.

23. **tying your shoelaces.** This is a **language type of question**. To find the answer you have to read the text carefully, especially the section that is quoted: a reef knot *can be used in many everyday situations* (see lines 2–3). An *everyday situation* is something that occurs more or less everyday such as tying your shoelaces.

24. **timid.** This is an **inferring type of question**. To find the answer you have to 'read between the lines'. You read *I was so scared I was hardly game to move* (see lines 20–21) and *It was waiting for me to go to sleep so it could come out and eat me* (see lines 29–31) and *Shaun watches, horrified* (see lines 51–52). Shaun is frightened of the bunyip. He is *timid* which means 'easily frightened or alarmed'.

25. **disbelieving** This is an **inferring type of question**. To find the answer you have to 'read between the lines'. You read that Ryan says *What? A bunyip? They're not real* (see lines 17–18) and *Good! That means I can prove how stupid you are!* (see lines 47–48). Ryan's words and his behaviour in looking under the bed suggests that he doesn't believe Shaun. He is disbelieving.

26. **He felt it pushing up on his mattress.** This is a **fact-finding type of question**. The answer is a fact in the text. You read *I felt it pushing up on the mattress* (see lines 19–20).

27. **He wanted Shaun to stop asking questions.** This is an **inferring type of question**. To find the answer you have to 'read between the lines'. You read *Now let me go to sleep* (see lines 25–26) and *I'm going to sleep. Listen! Zzzzz. Zzzzz* (see lines 40–41). This is pretend snoring. Ryan wanted Shaun to stop asking questions so Ryan could go to sleep.

28. **(3, 1, 4, 2).** This is a **fact-finding type of question**. The answer is a fact in the text. By reading the text carefully you will identify the correct order of events: 1. Ryan reads a book (*A book lies half-open on the bed* (see lines 3–4)). 2. Shaun makes sure Ryan is not asleep (*You awake Ryan?* (see line 7)). 3. Shaun warns Ryan about the monster under his bed

(*There's something under my bed ... bunyip* (see lines 13–16)). 4. *Ryan gasps loudly* (see line 54).

29. **He wanted to give Shaun a fright.** This is an **inferring type of question**. To find the answer you have to 'read between the lines'. You read *Ryan gasps loudly* (see line 54) which frightens Shaun and causes Ryan to laugh. He wanted to give Shaun a fright.

30. **had a vivid imagination.** This is an **inferring type of question**. To find the answer you have to 'read between the lines'. You read *There's something under my bed* (see lines 13–14)— Shaun thought there was a bunyip under the bed. You also read that Ryan says *They're not real* (see lines 17–18)—Ryan pointed out that bunyips are not real. Shaun also thought he felt something and heard something but Ryan, by looking under the bed, showed there was nothing there. Shaun has a vivid imagination.

31. **thrilled by the unexpected event.** This is an **inferring type of question**. To find the answer you have to 'read between the lines'. You can see that the seagulls went into the ocean to eat scraps they could find. Seagulls are scavengers and so they would be thrilled by the rubbish being discarded.

32. **False alarm.** This is an **inferring type of question**. To find the answer you have to 'read between the lines'. You can see by his beard and lack of clothes that the man has been marooned for a long time. In Frame 2 he is excitedly jumping about, trying to be rescued but the ship only comes to dump rubbish and in the last frame has disappeared.

33. **trying to attract attention.** This is an **inferring type of question**. To find the answer you have to 'read between the lines'. You can see that the man is jumping about and waving wildly. This is an action taken by desperate people trying to attract attention.

34. **dismayed.** This is an **inferring type of question**. To find the answer you have to 'read between the lines'. You can see that the man is not happy. There is rubbish dumped in the ocean and he hasn't been rescued. He is dismayed which means 'disappointed'.

35. **The oceans aren't giant rubbish dumps.** This is a **synthesis type of question**. To find the answer you have to look at the whole cartoon. The cartoon is more about environmental damage than the rescue of a person.

SAMPLE QUESTIONS—LANGUAGE CONVENTIONS

Instructions for teachers and parents

This section tests whether students can find spelling, grammar and punctuation errors in a text and whether they can write correctly. Most of the questions are multiple choice.

Sometimes they will have to write an answer. In all cases emphasise that they have to read each question carefully and study each answer option in order to choose the correct answer.

The spelling mistakes in these sentences have been circled.
Colour in the circle with the correct spelling.

1. Mr Jackson said he (shoud) catch the later bus.

   should ○   shude ○   shulde ○   shoulde ○

2. The church fete was very (successfull).

   sucessful ○   succesful ○   successful ○   successfull ○

3. Some bullocks were let (lose) in the streets of a town in Spain.

   louse ○   loose ○   loos ○   loss ○

4. "We won't go there (enyway)!" said Dad.

   annieway ○   annyway ○   anyweigh ○   anyway ○

5. We must (cheque) the rainwater tank for any disease.

   check ○   cheeck ○   checque ○   chech ○

6. Did Captain Cook (descover) Tasmania?

   decover ○   deskover ○   discuver ○   discover ○

7. Uncle Bertie took a picture of the (seene) from the main road.

   seen ○   scene ○   sciene ○   sean ○

8. Fifteen plus fifteen equals (therty).

   therety ○   thirtty ○   thirty ○   thierty ○

9. Do you, or don't you, (undastand) the rules?

   ○ undarstand
   ○ understand
   ○ understan
   ○ understant

☞ Answers and explanations on page 23

10. The Roman soldier had a (sheild) of iron.

shield ◯	sheeld ◯	shild ◯	schield ◯

11. Nancy has (freckels) but Kim has none.

freckells ◯	freckals ◯	frecals ◯	freckles ◯

Look at the labelled drawing. The spelling mistakes on the labels have been circled. Write the correct spelling of each word in the boxes.

12. a dark (color)

13. a fishing (trawlar)

14. boat (cabbin)

15. (refleckshun)

16. (warf)

Read *The small town of Broke*. Each line has one word that is incorrect. Write the correct spelling of each word in the boxes.

The small town of Broke

Broke is an odd name for a small villadge. It has just one shop,   **17.**

but it's a real supermarket. The one stoar offers such services as a   **18.**

petrol station, post office, grocery shelfs, fresh vegetables and fruit **19.**

and a take-away food outlet—a surprize in a small country town. **20.**

Each sentence has one word that is incorrect.
Write the correct spelling of each word in the boxes.

The rower in the small boat dropped an ankor near the reef. **21.**

An athlete atempted to break the world record. **22.**

There were five empty trollies outside the supermarket. **23.**

The death adder is a deadly Australian serpant. **24.**

I can't decide weather to wear shorts or blue jeans. **25.**

Colour in the circle with the correct answer.

26. Which word correctly completes this sentence?

Daniel took fruit from ████████ only tree in the garden!

a	and	the	that
◯	◯	◯	◯

27. Which sentence has the correct punctuation?
- ◯ The red blue and black colours of the sports team look smart.
- ◯ The red, blue and black colours of the sports team look smart.
- ◯ The red, blue, and black colours of the sports team look smart.
- ◯ The red, blue, and black, colours of the sports team look smart.

28. Which word correctly completes this sentence?

Neither my aunt nor my uncle ▨▨▨▨ arriving by train today.

are	am	were	is
○	○	○	○

29. Which word correctly completes this sentence?

The horse had ▨▨▨▨ him to the ground after the jump!

threw	threwed	throwed	thrown
○	○	○	○

30. A full stop (.) has been left out of these sentences.

Where should the missing full stop go?

This is your last chance Ben Mr Lee and the Olympic Committee are not impressed.

31. Which word correctly completes this sentence?

▨▨▨▨ Beverly had a headache she couldn't take her normal music class.

Although	However	Because	And
○	○	○	○

32. Which word uses the apostrophe correctly?

I checked the pen's. They were not Tanya's. Her's were tied with ribbon's.

33. Which word in this sentence is an adverb (adds meaning to a verb)?

The lonely girl dashed breathlessly along the beach at the break of day.

lonely	dashed	breathlessly	break
○	○	○	○

34. Which sentence has the correct punctuation?

○ The policewoman said that we had to wait for the road to be cleared.

○ The policewoman said, "that we had to wait for the road to be cleared."

○ The policewoman said, "That we had to wait for the road to be cleared."

○ The policewoman said that, "We had to wait for the road to be cleared."

35. Which sentence has the correct punctuation?

○ Get out!

○ What do you want!

○ Please pass the salt to grandma!

○ I am in year 4!

Read *Petanque*. The text has some gaps.
Choose the correct word or words to fill each gap.

Petanque

36. Petanque is a _____, a bit like a cross between lawn bowls and marbles which is played on hard dirt, gravel or grass.

○ french game
○ French Game
○ french Game
○ French game

37. Players stand inside a circle _____ throw metal balls as close as possible to a small wooden ball.

and	but	or	than
○	○	○	○

38. The metal balls are about the size of a cricket ball. _____, the wooden ball is only the size of a large marble.

Although	however	although	However
○	○	○	○

39. Petanque is played by two, _____ or six players in two teams. Players have three balls, except for teams of three players who only have two balls each.

four,	four.	four	Four,
○	○	○	○

Colour in the circle(s) with the correct answer.

40. Which word correctly completes this sentence?

You ______ use the vacuum cleaner on the front path!

cant	ca'nt	cann't	can't
○	○	○	○

41. Two commas (,) have been left out of this sentence.
Where should the missing commas go?

My eldest brother ↑ Gavin ↑ was seen running ↑ down the street after a stray grey ↑ dog.

42. Which words can all be adjectives (describing words)?

- ○ jump, writing, called, think
- ○ happy, lost, twenty, clear
- ○ sorrow, team, gas, Adelaide
- ○ above, on, beside, underneath

43. Which word correctly completes this sentence?

Do most people prefer hamburgers ______ pizzas?

from	to	by	for
○	○	○	○

44. Which word correctly completes this sentence?

Carmen purchased three ______ then left them in the shop.

Cds	CDs	CD's	cd's
○	○	○	○

45. Which word correctly completes this sentence?

Our team of netballers ______ ready whenever you are.

was	are	is	were
○	○	○	○

46. Which word or words correctly complete this sentence?

I saw a wrapper on my desk and wondered ______ it was.

whose	who's	whose's	who is
○	○	○	○

Answers and explanations on page 24

47. Which words correctly complete this sentence?

We still had to walk to our uncle's place ▭ .

- ○ but the weather was bad
- ○ either we did or we didn't
- ○ whether it rained or was fine
- ○ what was a long way

48. Which words or letters should have brackets in this sentence?

The people from <u>Papua New Guinea</u> <u>PNG</u> are arriving <u>in Perth</u> <u>on 23 May</u>.

    ↑   ↑   ↑   ↑

    ○   ○   ○   ○

49. Which words correctly complete this sentence?

My father, with his sunglasses on, ▭ .

- ○ and my mother in her sun hat
- ○ with the silver rims
- ○ sat patiently in the car
- ○ during a traffic accident on the highway

50. Which sentence has the correct punctuation?

- ○ "I don't care," she said. "what you think about it.
- ○ "I don't care," she said, "what you think about it."
- ○ "I don't care." she said, "what you think about it."
- ○ "I don't care," she said, "What you think about it."

END OF QUESTIONS

Well done! You have completed the sample questions for Language Conventions. Even if you don't practise any other Language Conventions Tests, at least you will have some familiarity with the method used in the NAPLAN tests.

How did you go with these sample questions? Check to see where you did well and where you had problems. Try to revise the questions that were hard for you.

There are four more Language Conventions tests to practise. These each contain around 50 questions. They include many of the same types of questions, plus a few other types.

☞ Answers and explanations on page 24

1. **should.** *Should* has a silent *l*. It has a similar spelling to *would* and *could*.

2. **successful.** The suffix *ful* is always spelled with a single *l*.

3. **loose.** Do not confuse *lose* (lost) with *loose*. *Loose* rhymes with *moose*.

4. **anyway.** *Anyway* is a compound word: *any + way*. Make sure you pronounce it correctly.

5. **check.** *Check* and *cheque* are homonyms: words that sound the same which are spelled differently. A *cheque* is a written payment for an amount of money.

6. **discover.** *Discover* is the word *cover* with the prefix *dis* (*dis + cover*).

7. **scene.** *Seen* and *scene* are homonyms: words that sound the same which are spelled differently. *Scene* refers to a view.

8. **thirty.** Take care with *er* and *ir* in words. They both have the same sound.

9. **understand.** *Understand* is a compound word: *under + stand*.

10. **shield.** Remember: as a general rule, it is *i* before *e* except after a *c* sound. Remember also that there are quite a few exceptions to this rule.

11. **freckles.** *ckle* is a common ending in many words (e.g. *trickle*, *cackle*). The *al* ending is often used for adjectives (e.g. *global*, *coastal*).

12. **colour.** *Colour* should be spelled the Australian way with *our*, not the American way (*or*).

13. **trawler.** It is easy to confuse *ar* and *er* endings. *Er* is often used with people or occupations.

14. **cabin.** There is no double *bb* in *cabin*.

15. **reflection.** *Reflection* is *re + flec + tion*. The *tion* ending often has a *shun* sound.

16. **wharf.** Remember: *wharf* has a silent *h*.

17. **village.** Remember to pronounce the word correctly.

18. **store.** The letter combinations *oar* and *ore* have the same sound. Remember when to use them correctly.

19. **shelves.** Many common words that end with *f* make the plural by dropping the *f* and adding *ves* (e.g. *wolf* → *wolves*).

20. **surprise.** Do not confuse the *prise* in *surprise* with *prize*.

21. **anchor.** *Anchor* is a fairly simple word if pronounced carefully, but be careful with the silent *h*.

22. **attempted.** Think of *attempted* as *at + tempt + ed*. This way you will be less likely to leave out a *t*.

23. **trolleys.** One *trolley* → two *trolleys*. Because *trolley* has a vowel before the *y*, simply add an *s* for the plural.

24. **serpent.** Remember to pronounce the word carefully: *serpent*.

25. **whether.** *Whether* and *weather* are homonyms: words that sound the same which are spelled differently. *Weather* refers to the daily state of atmospheric conditions.

26. **the.** *The* is a definite article. In the question, *the* refers to a specific tree that has been identified.

27. **The red, blue and black colours of the sports team look smart.** Commas are used in a series of adjectives where there are more than two adjectives. *And* is used between the last two adjectives in the series or list.

28. **is.** Two singular subjects connected by *or* or *nor* require a singular verb.

29. **thrown.** *Threw* is an irregular verb. Most verbs in English form their past tense by adding *ed* (e.g. *he looked*). There are a number of irregular verbs when this doesn't happen. So *thrown* is the past tense of *threw*, not 'threwed'. With *thrown* you need a 'helper'—another verb to 'help' it. *Had* can be the helping verb.

30. **This is your last chance Ben. Mr Lee and the Olympic Committee are not impressed.** There are two main ideas in the text. They are separated by a full stop. It is a good idea to read the text silently to sense where there is a definite pause.

31. **Because** *Because* is a conjunction. In this sentence, *because* connects a reason to a reaction—a headache and missing a class.

32. **Tanya's.** *Tanya's* is the only word showing ownership with an apostrophe. *Hers* is a possessive pronoun and does not require an apostrophe.

33. **breathlessly.** Adverbs add meaning to verbs. *Breathlessly* explains how the girl ran. Many adverbs end in *ly* but not all *ly* words are adverbs.

34. **The policewoman said that we had to wait for the road to be cleared.** This is an example of indirect speech and no speech marks are required. The actual words spoken are not recorded.

35. **Get out!** *Get out!* is the best example of an exclamation sentence.

36. **French game.** *French* is a proper adjective, while *game* is a common noun.

37. **and.** The word *and* is a conjunction used to indicate an additional fact.

38. **However.** *However* has a capital as it is the start of a new sentence. It is an adverb introducing a contrasting statement.

39. **four** There is no comma after *four*. A comma is used to separate adjectives in a series, except when a conjunction (*or*) separates the last two adjectives.

40. **can't.** *Can't* is a contraction (shortened word) for *cannot*. The apostrophe indicates that the letter **no** have been left out.

41. **My eldest brother, Gavin, was seen running down the street after a stray grey dog.** As the writer can only have one eldest brother, commas are needed around the brother's name because the name is an additional, unnecessary fact that could be left out of the sentence.

42. **happy, lost, twenty, clear.** These words can all be used to describe a noun.

43. **to.** *To* is the correct preposition. *From* is a common speech error. Certain prepositions tend to go with certain verbs. They have to be learned and remembered.

44. **CDs.** No apostrophe is required because there is no sense of ownership. The **s** indicates the plural form. CD is an acronym which stands for the first letters of *compact disc*: both letters should be capitalised.

45. **is.** Subjects and verbs must agree with one another in number. If a subject is singular (*team* **not** *netballers*), its verb must also be singular (*is*); if a subject is plural, its verb must be plural. *Team* is a single collective noun.

46. **whose.** *Whose* is a possessive pronoun and does not require an apostrophe. *Who's* is the shortened form of *who is*.

47. **whether it rained or was fine.** *Whether* is a conjunction used to indicate some element of doubt regarding two possibilities.

48. **PNG.** Brackets are used for abbreviations to provide an opportunity to use the shortened term later in the passage.

49. **sat patiently in the car.** This group of words contains a verb (*sat*) which is essential for a simple sentence to make sense.

50. **"I don't care," she said, "what you think about it."** The only full stop required is at the end of the sentence. A capital letter follows a full stop. When a credit for speech comes in the middle of quoted language, it is set apart from the actual words spoken.

NUMERACY TEST 1

This is the first Numeracy Test. Please note that the Year 5 NAPLAN Numeracy Test has 40 questions to be completed in 50 minutes. In order to build confidence, we have provided 35 questions in Tests 1 and 2 to be completed in 45 minutes.

If you aren't sure what to do, ask your teacher or your parents to help you. Don't be afraid to ask if it isn't clear to you.

Depending on the question, either write your answer in the box or colour in the circle with the correct answer. Colour in only one circle for each answer.

1. Jack collects matchboxes.

He laid them on a table, making 2 piles of 6 matchboxes each.

He then picked up all the matchboxes and put them into 3 equal piles.

How many matchboxes were in each pile?

1	2	3	4
○	○	○	○

2. It is now 3:15.

Caleb's friend is coming to his house in half an hour.

At what time will his friend arrive?

○ half past 3　　○ twenty past 3

○ twenty to 4　　○ quarter to 4

3. Thomas runs 3 kilometres each day.

How far does he run in 6 days?

18 km	9 km	2 km	3 km
○	○	○	○

4. Which of these number sentences equals 32?

○ $8 \times 3 + 1$　　○ $15 + 16$

○ half of 48　　○ $5 \times 8 - 8$

5. The pocket money received by four friends is shown in the table.

Name	Pocket money
Brayden	$15
Ethan	$44
Jaidee	$14
Kai	$9

What was the difference between the pocket money given to Ethan and Kai?

$ [   ]　Write your answer in the box.

6.

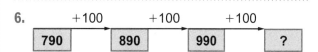

+100		+100		+100	
790		890		990		?

What is the missing number?

[   ]　Write your answer in the box.

7.

March

S	M	T	W	T	F	S
				1	2	3
4	5	6	7	8	9	10
11	12	13	14	15	16	17
18	19	20	21	22	23	24
25	26	27	28	29	30	31

What is the date of the third Tuesday on this calendar?

○ 13 March　　○ 20 March

○ 15 March　　○ 22 March

☞ Answers and explanations on page 156

8. Shannon has 22 cards and gives 13 away.
How many cards does she still have?

Write your answer in the box.

9. Craig shaded one-third of a shape.
Which shape did he shade?

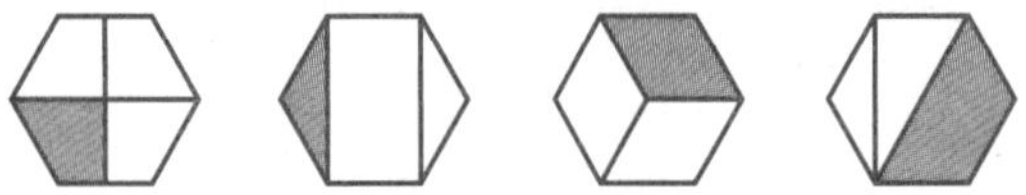

○   ○   ○   ○

10. A number line is drawn below.

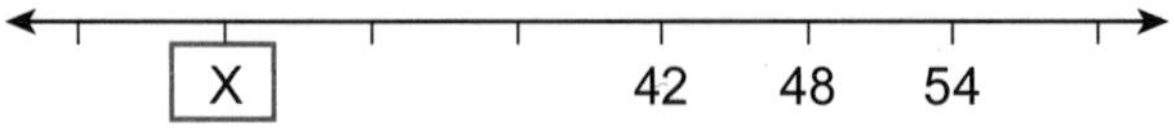

X   42   48   54

What is the missing number (shown as X)?

Write your answer in the box.

11. **1827 ÷ 9 =** ?

What is the missing number?

23   203   2003   230
○   ○   ○   ○

12. Which of these nets will **not** form a cube?

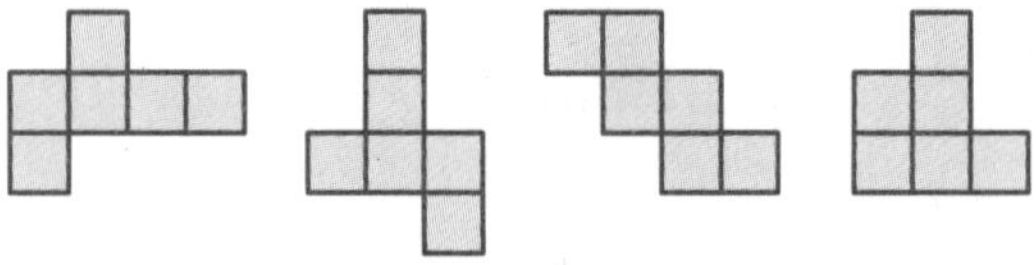

○   ○   ○   ○

13. Darryl used matchsticks to make a pattern of triangles like this.

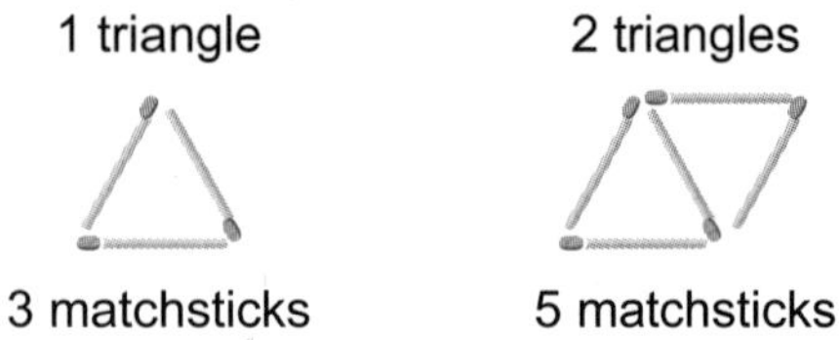

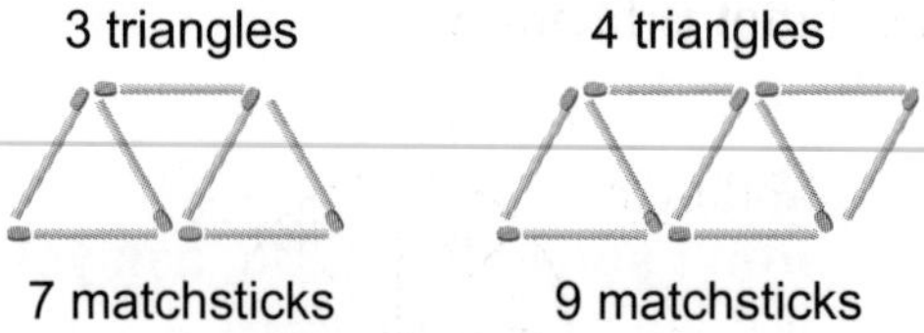

1 triangle   2 triangles

3 matchsticks   5 matchsticks

3 triangles   4 triangles

7 matchsticks   9 matchsticks

He continued the pattern.

How many matchsticks will he need to make 8 triangles in this pattern?

14   15   16   17
○   ○   ○   ○

14. Which of these is the number:

two hundred and eighty thousand and sixty-seven?

208 067   280 670   2867   280 067
○   ○   ○   ○

15. Billy spent $48 on train tickets.

If each ticket cost $6, how many tickets did he buy?

Write your answer in the box.

16. 6   0   4   7   1

What is the largest possible number using all five digits?

Write your answer in the box.

17. A number pattern starting at 3 is formed using the rule:

'Double the number and add 2'.

Amie writes the first four numbers:

3, 8, 18, 38.

What is the next number in the pattern?

Write your answer in the box.

18. Labinot is facing West.

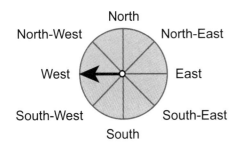

He then turns a quarter-turn in an anti-clockwise direction.

Which direction is he now facing?

○ North-West   ○ South-West

○ North   ○ South

---

19. What is the missing number?

| 45 | + | ? | = | 110 |

Write your answer in the box.

---

20. Five numbers are written on cards.

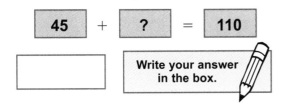

The cards are then arranged from lowest to highest.

Which number is written on the middle card?

Write your answer in the box.

---

21. The map shows the roads between the City and surrounding towns.

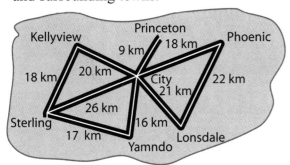

Jamil drives from Princeton through the City to Sterling.

How far does he drive?

☐ km   Write your answer in the box.

---

22. Here is a menu for meals at a restaurant.

Entrees		Mains		Desserts	
Prawn cocktail	$9.90	Steak	$23.90	Pavlova	$7.90
Soup	$7.70	Chicken	$21.90	Apple pie	$6.90
Oysters	$10.90	Fish	$19.90	Sundae	$4.70

Josie ordered the Prawn cocktail, the Chicken and a Sundae.

What is the best estimate for the cost of her meal?

$35 $40 $25 $30

○   ○   ○   ○

---

23. Which of these shapes does **not** have a line of symmetry?

○   ○   ○   ○

24.

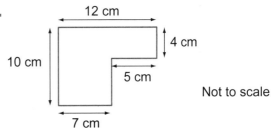

12 cm

4 cm

10 cm

5 cm

Not to scale

7 cm

What is the perimeter of the shape?

38 cm   40 cm   43 cm   44 cm

○   ○   ○   ○

25.

	?	1
−	4	2
	3	?

What are the missing numbers?

☐ and ☐

Write your answer in the boxes.

26. Here is a pattern of repeating shapes.
Each of the shapes has been numbered.

1 2 3 4

5 6 7 8

What is the name of the 19th shape?

○ triangle   ○ trapezium

○ pentagon   ○ hexagon

27. Here are four numbered cards.

8 6 1 5

Use two of the cards to form a number that is a multiple of 7.

☐ Write your answer in the box.

28.

A notebook costs $1.60.

Belinda pays $5.00 for a notebook and two pens.

What is the cost of one pen?

$1.70 $1.80 $2.20 $2.40
○   ○   ○   ○

29. A shape is made from squares.
Four-fifths of the shape is to be shaded.

How many squares will be shaded?

4   8   12   16
○   ○   ○   ○

30. Here are the prices for some sandwiches, pieces of fruit and drinks.

Sandwiches		Fruit		Drinks	
Cheese	60 cents	Apple	50 cents	Juice	80 cents
Salad	80 cents	Orange	60 cents	Water	70 cents
Ham	70 cents	Banana	40 cents	Milk	90 cents

Jannah bought a cheese sandwich and a bottle of water.

How much change will she receive from $2.00?

☐ cents   Write your answer in the box.

31. Julia made a spinner where the chance of spinning a green is most likely and there is an equal chance of spinning a red or a blue.

Which of these is Julia's spinner?

○   ○

☞ Answers and explanations on pages 156–157

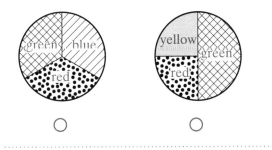

○   ○

32. A bakery sells bags of bread rolls for $5.

Each bag holds 8 bread rolls.

What is the cost of 2 dozen bread rolls?

$ [   ]    **Write your answer in the box.**

33. Abdul made this timeline for next Saturday.

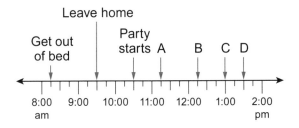

The party lasts for two and a half hours.

Which letter represents the time the party finishes?

A   B   C   D
○   ○   ○   ○

34. A fruit shop sells the following:

| Tomatoes $4 per kg | Mandarines 6 for $4 |
| Apples $3 per bag | Cucumbers $1.50 each |

Find the cost of 12 mandarines and 2 cucumbers?

[   ]   **Write your answer in the box.**

35. David spends $5 on school supplies. He bought at least one of each of these items.

Item	Price	Number
Pen	$0.80	
Pencil	$0.70	
Ruler	$1.30	
Eraser	$1.40	

Write in the column the number of each item David buys.

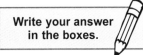 **Write your answer in the boxes.**

END OF TEST

Well done! You have completed the first Numeracy Test. Even if you don't practise any others, at least you will have done a fair sample of the questions.

How did you go with these test questions? Some were harder than the sample questions. Check to see where you did well and where you had problems. Try to revise the questions that were hard for you.

Use the diagnostic chart on pages 31–32 to see which level of ability you reached. This is only an estimate. Don't be surprised if you answered some difficult questions correctly or even missed some easier questions.

There are now three more practice tests, each containing 35 or 40 questions. We will start to include new types of questions in each of these tests.

☞ **Answers and explanations on page 157**

Instructions

Please go back and read the introduction on page vi to *How we help you work out your student's level of ability*.

Check the answers

As you check the answer for each question, mark it as correct (✓) or incorrect (✗). Mark any questions that you omitted or left out as incorrect (✗) for the moment.

Then look at how many you answered correctly in each level. Your level of ability is the point where you started having consistent difficulty with questions. For example, if you answered most questions correctly up to the Intermediate level and then got most questions wrong from then onwards, it is likely your ability is at an Intermediate level. You can ask your parents or your teacher to help you do this if it isn't clear.

We expect you to miss some easy questions and also to answer some hard questions correctly, but your level of ability should be where you are starting to find the questions too hard. Some students will reach the top level—this means that their ability cannot be measured by these questions or even the NAPLAN Tests. They found it far too easy.

Understanding the different levels

We have divided the questions into three levels of difficulty:

- Basic
- Intermediate
- Advanced.

For each question we have described the skill involved in answering the question. Then, depending on what sort of skill is involved, we have placed it into one of the three levels. It should make sense, especially when you go back and look at the type of question. The Basic level includes the easiest tasks and then they increase in difficulty.

The purpose of these practice tests is to help you be as confident as possible and perform to the best of your ability. The purpose of the NAPLAN Tests is to show what you know or can do. For the first time the user can estimate his or her level of ability before taking the actual test and see if there is any improvement across the practice tests.

Remember that the levels of ability are only a rough guide. No claim is made that they are perfect. They are only an indicator. Your level might change as you do each practice test. We hope that these brief notes are of some help.

Instructions

- As you check the answer for each question, mark it as correct (✓) or incorrect (✗). Mark any questions that you omitted or left out as incorrect (✗) for the moment.
- Then look at how many you answered correctly in each level.
- You will be able to see what level you are at by finding the point where you started having consistent difficulty with questions. For example, if you answered most questions correctly up to the Intermediate level and then got most questions wrong from then onwards, it is likely your ability is at an Intermediate level. You can ask your parents or your teacher to help you do this if it isn't clear to you.

Am I able to ...

	SKILL	ESTIMATED LEVEL	✓ or ✗
1	Use knowledge of number facts involving multiplication to determine equal values?	Basic	
2	Convert digital time to analog time?	Basic	
3	Solve a problem involving multiplication?	Basic	
4	Use knowledge of mathematical operations to compare number sentences?	Basic	
5	Interpret data in a table to solve a subtraction problem?	Basic	
6	Continue a number pattern involving counting on by hundreds?	Basic	
7	Identify a specific date on a calendar?	Basic	
8	Solve a word problem involving subtraction?	Basic	
9	Recognise a common fraction of an object?	Basic	
10	Identify a number on a number line?	Basic	
11	Apply place value knowledge to complete a number sentence involving division?	Intermediate	
12	Identify the net of a cube?	Intermediate	
13	Continue a spatial pattern beyond the next term?	Intermediate	
14	Convert words to numerals for very large numbers?	Intermediate	
15	Solve a word problem involving division?	Intermediate	
16	Apply knowledge of place value to compare large numbers?	Intermediate	
17	Continue a number pattern involving two-step calculation?	Intermediate	
18	Specify direction using anti-clockwise quarter turns?	Intermediate	
19	Use problem-solving strategies to complete a number sentence?	Intermediate	
20	Arrange numbers in order of magnitude?	Intermediate	
21	Use a map to find the distance between locations?	Intermediate	
22	Solve everyday money problems involving estimation and addition?	Intermediate	
23	Identify all lines of symmetry in a shape?	Intermediate	
24	Calculate the perimeter of a composite rectangular shape?	Advanced	
25	Solve a problem by applying knowledge of place value and number properties?	Advanced	
26	Continue a pattern involving geometric shapes?	Advanced	
27	Use knowledge of multiples to form two-digit numbers?	Advanced	

	SKILL	ESTIMATED LEVEL	✓ or ✗
28	Solve everyday money problems involving multiplication and division?	Advanced	
29	Divide whole objects into fractions?	Advanced	
30	Solve everyday money problems involving addition and subtraction?	Advanced	
31	Use chance terms to develop an experiment involving a spinner?	Advanced	
32	Solve everyday money problems involving multiplication and division?	Advanced	
33	Locate information on a timeline?	Advanced	
34	Solve money problems using multiplication and addition?	Advanced	
35	Complete a table using information?	Advanced	

NUMERACY TEST 2

This is the second Numeracy Test. There are 35 questions.

If you aren't sure what to do, ask your teacher or your parents to help you. Don't be afraid to ask if it isn't clear to you.

Allow around 45 minutes for this test.

Write the answer in the box or colour in the circle with the correct answer. Colour in only one circle for each answer.

---

1. Kai has $12 more than Lizzie.

If Kai has $18, how much has Lizzie?

Write your answer in the box.

2. Owen is older than Pamela, but younger than Charmaine.

If Pamela is 12 years old and Charmaine is 15 years old, what could be Owen's age?

- ◯ 3 years old
- ◯ 11 years old
- ◯ 13 years old
- ◯ 16 years old

3. There are four shaded shapes below.

Which has an area of 10 square units?

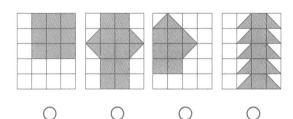

◯　　◯　　◯　　◯

4. Five players in a soccer team scored goals during a season.

Goals scored	
Name	**Goals**
Laura	7
Jonathon	3
Carrie	12
Caleb	5
Robbie	11

What is the difference between the number of goals scored by Carrie and Jonathon?

Write your answer in the box.

5. Karen recorded in the table the number of SMSs she sent in one week.

Day	Tally marks
Sunday	⊞ IIII
Monday	IIII
Tuesday	⊞
Wednesday	⊞ I
Thursday	⊞
Friday	IIII
Saturday	⊞ III

How many SMSs did she send altogether on Friday and Saturday?

10　　11　　12　　17
◯　　◯　　◯　　◯

6. How many edges does a square pyramid have?

4　　8　　10　　12
◯　　◯　　◯　　◯

☞ **Answers and explanations on page 157**

7. A birthday cake was bought for $27.50.
What was the change from $40?

8. The difference between two numbers is 6.

If the smaller number is 9, what is the larger number?

3	13	15	17
○	○	○	○

9. On two days last week it rained.

Dave measured the rain in his gauge.

On Thursday he measured 14 mm and on Saturday 16 mm.

What was the total rainfall?

☐ mm   **Write your answer in the box.**

10. What is the next number in this pattern?

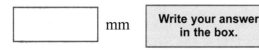

| 45 | 70 | 95 | |

└→ +25 ─┘ └→ +25 ─┘ └→ +25 ─┘

☐   **Write your answer in the box.**

11. Grandma turned 68 in 2000.

In what year was Grandma born?

1942	1938	1932	1928
○	○	○	○

12. Matchsticks are used to form squares as shown in the figures below.

Figure 1   Figure 2   Figure 3

If the pattern continued, how many matchsticks would be used in Figure 5?

16	17	20	15
○	○	○	○

13. A train leaves Bilpin at the time shown on the clock on the right.

The train arrives in Essex 20 minutes later.

Which clock shows the time it arrives?

8:23	8:35	8:45	8:55
○	○	○	○

14. Here is a multiplication grid with two missing numbers.

×	3	5	?	8
2	6	10	12	16
4	12	20	24	32
?	21	35	42	56
9	27	45	54	72

What are the two missing numbers?

☐ and ☐   **Write your answer in the boxes.**

15. These numbers are in a pattern and they increase by the same amount.

4	?	?	28

What are the missing numbers?

[ ] and [ ]

Write your answer in the boxes.

16. Karen has three identical discs.

She places them on a balance with two blocks.

The masses of the blocks are 200 grams and 500 grams.

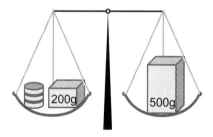

What is the mass of each of Karen's discs?

[ ] g

Write your answer in the box.

17. Nerida buys a metre of ribbon.

She uses 14 centimetres from the roll to wrap a present.

How much ribbon remains on the roll?

960 cm   96 cm   860 cm   86 cm
○   ○   ○   ○

18. Here is a sequence of numbers.

15, 30, 45, 60, …

How many of these numbers will be in the sequence?

70	75	80	85	90	95

2   3   4   5
○   ○   ○   ○

19. Here is a sheet of stickers.

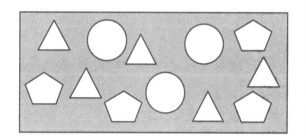

Magda has six identical sheets of stickers.

What is the total number of pentagon stickers?

[ ] pentagons

Write your answer in the box.

20. Rebecca has these coins.

How much more does she need to make $5.00?

$1.20 $1.30 $2.30 $2.20
○   ○   ○   ○

21. Steve wrote these numbers on cards and laid them on a table.

8	12	26	38	25
18	22	17	27	9
15	21	32	34	6

He picked up all the cards that have a factor of 3.

☞ **Answers and explanations on page 157**

How many cards will remain on the table?

12	15	10	8
○	○	○	○

22. Students at a school are raising money for a charity's Winter Appeal.

The table shows the money raised by each of the year groups.

Class	Fundraising total
Year 2	$60
Year 3	$240
Year 4	$480
Year 5	$120
Year 6	$300

Which of these statements is correct?

○ Year 2 has raised half as much as Year 4.

○ Year 6 has raised twice as much as Year 5.

○ Year 4 has raised four times as much as Year 5.

○ Year 3 has raised half as much as Year 5.

23. Miranda made this pattern by rotating the image a quarter of a turn in an **anti-clockwise** direction.

Which of these is the last image?

○ ○ ○ ○

24. Here is a number line.

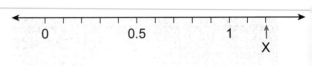

Which decimal is X pointing to?

Write your answer in the box.

25.

The map shows the roads joining four towns.

The distance from Knightly to Shirley is 45 kilometres.

What is the scale used on the map?

○ 1 unit = 15 km   ○ 1 unit = 5 km

○ 1 unit = 20 km   ○ 1 unit = 25 km

26. $16 + 5 < 4 \times \boxed{}$

Which of these numbers can be written in the box to make the number sentence true?

5	7	3	4
○	○	○	○

27 In a junior soccer club there are 5 boys registered for every 3 girls.

If the total number of registered girls is 60, how many boys are registered with the club?

 Write your answer in the box.

28. This net forms a cube.

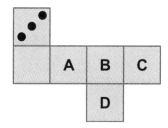

When the cube is formed each pair of opposite faces add to 7.

Where would the be?

   A   B   C   D
   ○   ○   ○   ○

29. Year 4 students were asked what they had eaten for breakfast.

	Boys	Girls
Cereal	8	5
Toast	3	6
Yoghurt	4	3

How many students had eaten cereal for breakfast?

   8   5   13   15
   ○   ○   ○   ○

Write your answer in the box.

30. Rianna wants to put 46 jelly beans into bags.

When she puts 6 jelly beans in each bag she has 4 left over.

How many bags did Rianna use?

   4   7   8   6
   ○   ○   ○   ○

31. There were 6 checkouts open at the supermarket.

There were 3 customers at 4 of the checkouts and 2 at the other checkouts.

How many customers were there **altogether**?

 Write your answer in the box.

32. A bag contains black balls and white balls.

When Jeremy takes a ball from the bag he is more likely to choose a white ball than a black ball.

Which could be Jeremy's bag of balls?

  ○   ○   ○   ○

☞ Answers and explanations on page 158

33. The graph shows the number of goals scored by Louise, Kimberley, Breanna and Tamara.

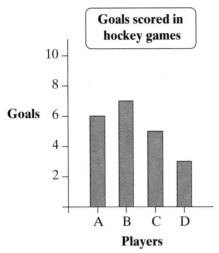

Goals scored in hockey games

- Breanna scored 3 goals.
- Tamara scored the most goals.
- Kimberley scored 1 more goal than Louise.

On the graph, who is player C?

○ Louise

○ Kimberley

○ Breanna

○ Tamara

34. This shape is made from identical squares. What is the perimeter of the shape?

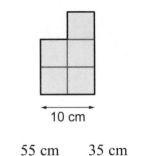

10 cm

45 cm   55 cm   35 cm   50 cm

○   ○   ○   ○

35. The diagram shows a solid made from 15 identical cubes.

The solid is then painted.

After the paint dries, the cube is pulled apart.

How many of the cubes will have exactly 3 faces painted?

_____ cubes

Write your answer in the box.

END OF TEST

Well done! You have completed the second Numeracy Test. We tried to change the questions and some were a little harder.

How did you go with these test questions? Check to see where you did well and where you had problems. Try to revise the questions that were hard for you.

Use the diagnostic chart on pages 39–40 to see which level of ability you reached. This is only an estimate. Don't be surprised if you answered some difficult questions correctly or even missed some easier questions.

There are now two more practice tests, each containing 40 questions. We have included some new types of questions in this test.

CHECK YOUR SKILLS: NUMERACY TEST 2

Instructions

- As you check the answer for each question, mark it as correct (✓) or incorrect (✗). Mark any questions that you omitted or left out as incorrect (✗) for the moment.
- Then look at how many you answered correctly in each level.
- You will be able to see what level you are at by finding the point where you started having consistent difficulty with questions. For example, if you answered most questions correctly up to the Intermediate level and then got most questions wrong from then onwards, it is likely your ability is at an Intermediate level. You can ask your parents or your teacher to help you do this if it isn't clear to you.

Am I able to ...

	SKILL	ESTIMATED LEVEL	✓ or ✗
1	Solve a problem using subtraction?	Basic	
2	Recognise order of magnitude from descriptions?	Basic	
3	Measure area by counting whole- and half-grid squares?	Basic	
4	Interpret data in a table to solve a subtraction problem?	Basic	
5	Interpret data in a table to solve an addition problem?	Basic	
6	Identify the features of a 3D model?	Basic	
7	Solve a money problem involving subtraction?	Basic	
8	Solve a word problem involving numbers less than 20?	Basic	
9	Solve a word problem involving adding two-digit numbers?	Basic	
10	Complete a number pattern by adding a two-digit number?	Basic	
11	Use strategies to solve a word problem involving a four-digit number?	Intermediate	
12	Continue a spatial pattern beyond the next term?	Intermediate	
13	Solve a problem involving both analog and digital time?	Intermediate	
14	Use your knowledge of multiples to solve a problem?	Intermediate	
15	Find the missing numbers in a number pattern by finding the difference?	Intermediate	
16	Use strategies to determine the mass of objects using a balance?	Intermediate	
17	Solve a word problem using subtraction from 100?	Intermediate	
18	Continue a number pattern to identify missing numbers?	Intermediate	
19	Recognise common 2D shapes?	Intermediate	
20	Calculate the total value of coins to find the amount of change?	Intermediate	
21	Use an understanding of multiples to solve a problem?	Intermediate	
22	Interpret data in a table using multiplication?	Intermediate	
23	Continue a pattern involving anti-clockwise quarter-turns?	Intermediate	
24	Identify the location of a decimal on a number line?	Advanced	
25	Determine the scale used on a map?	Advanced	

	SKILL	ESTIMATED LEVEL	✓ or ✗
26	Find the missing number in a number sentence involving an inequality?	Advanced	
27	Solve a problem using a scale?	Advanced	
28	Using a net, determine the opposite faces of a cube?	Advanced	
29	Make conclusions using a two-way table?	Advanced	
30	Solve a word problem by changing to a number sentence?	Advanced	
31	Apply strategies such as multiplication or grouping to solve a word problem?	Advanced	
32	Use chance terms to describe the outcome in a simple experiment involving random selection?	Advanced	
33	Match word descriptions to label a column graph?	Advanced	
34	Calculate the perimeter of a composite rectangular shape?	Advanced	
35	Visualise the number of painted faces of a composite 3D object?	Advanced	

NUMERACY TEST 3

This is the third Numeracy Test. In order for you to fully prepare for next year's tests, we have provided 40 questions in Tests 3 and 4 to be completed in 50 minutes. This is the same as the Year 5 NAPLAN Numeracy Test.

If you aren't sure what to do, ask your teacher or your parents to help you. Don't be afraid to ask if it isn't clear to you.

Write the answer in the box or colour in the circle with the correct answer. Colour in only one circle for each answer.

1. The table shows the number of students who were absent from class in one week.

Day	Boys	Girls
Monday	0	2
Tuesday	3	2
Wednesday	1	3
Thursday	2	1
Friday	0	1

On which day were the most students absent?

○ Monday   ○ Tuesday

○ Wednesday   ○ Friday

2. Jayne bought a bottle of juice which cost $2.35.

How much change will she receive from $3.00?

[ ] cents   **Write your answer in the box.**

3. How many axes of symmetry does the road sign have?

   0   1   2   3

   ○   ○   ○   ○

4. A Farmer's Market is always on the last Sunday of the month.

Which date in February is the Farmer's Market?

Hint: use the calendar.

○ 20 February   ○ 27 February

○ 19 February   ○ 26 February

5. Which one of these shapes is a pentagon?

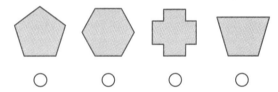

○   ○   ○   ○

6. Which shape covers the greatest area?

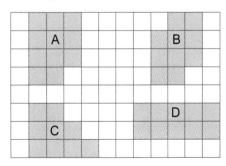

   A   B   C   D

   ○   ○   ○   ○

☞ Answers and explanations on page 158

7. Which one of these shapes is a cone?

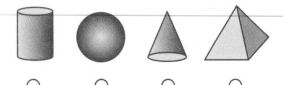

○   ○   ○   ○

8. Here is a picture of a tricycle.

Which of these number sentences shows how to find the number of wheels on 6 tricycles?

6 × 3   6 ÷ 3   6 + 3   6 − 3

○   ○   ○   ○

9. Which of these numbers is closest to 600?

555   640   609   700

○   ○   ○   ○

10. A basketball team has 5 players.

How many teams can be formed using 30 players?

25   35   6   150

○   ○   ○   ○

11. Here are five cards.

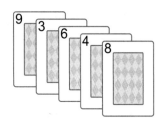

What is the total of the five cards?

Write your answer in the box.

12.

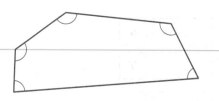

How many angles in the shape measure less than a right angle?

1   2   3   4

○   ○   ○   ○

13.

How many of these numbers are factors of 8?

Write your answer in the box.

14. The graph shows the passengers on a bus.

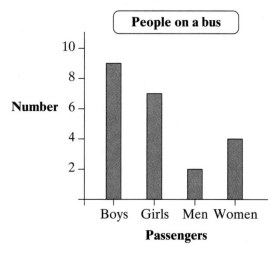

Which statement is true?

○ There were more girls on the bus than boys.

○ There were fewer women on the bus than men.

○ There were more boys on the bus than women.

○ There were fewer girls on the bus than women.

☞ Answers and explanations on page 158

15.

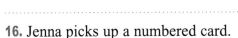

What are the missing numbers?

[   ] and [   ]

> **Write your answer in the boxes.**

16. Jenna picks up a numbered card.

She gives these clues about her number to her classmates.

| It is larger than 20. | It is a multiple of 6. |

| It is less than 40. | One of its factors is 5. |

What is her number?

[   ]

> **Write your answer in the box.**

17. What is the place value of 4 in the number 304 816?

- ○ four hundred thousand
- ○ forty thousand
- ○ four thousand
- ○ four hundred

18. Which of these is **not** true?

- ○ $10 - 4 < 2 + 5$
- ○ $100 \div 2 > 12 + 7$
- ○ $4^2 = 8 \times 2$
- ○ $10^2 + 3 > 12^2$

19. The table shows the birthdays of a group of friends.

Name	Birthday
Sue	1 April
Jannah	29 March
Carolyn	27 April
Ross	15 January
Chris	2 October
Helen	23 November

Who has their birthday next after Ross?

Carolyn	Jannah	Helen	Chris
○	○	○	○

20. Two of these shapes have the same number of faces.

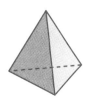
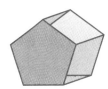

Shape 1   Shape 2

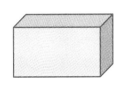

Shape 3   Shape 4

Which are the two shapes?

[   ] and [   ]

> **Write your answer in the boxes.**

21. Buffy is 9 years old.

Her mother is 4 times her age and her grandmother is 7 times her age.

What is the difference between the ages of her mother and grandmother?

○ 36 years   ○ 27 years

○ 63 years   ○ 49 years

22. A brick is 9 centimetres thick.

9 cm

Bricks are laid in three rows to form a wall.

What is the height of the wall?

27 cm   36 cm   54 cm   60 cm

○   ○   ○   ○

23. Ben has 16 stickers and Bill has 24 stickers.

The boys want to have an equal number of stickers.

Which statement describes what has to happen?

○ Ben gives Bill 4 stickers.

○ Ben gives Bill 8 stickers.

○ Bill gives Ben 8 stickers.

○ Bill gives Ben 4 stickers.

24. Ahn thinks of a number.

When he adds 40 to the number he gets 260.

What is Ahn's number?

[   ]   Write your answer in the box.

25. Brody and Kirstie are standing in a line at a bus stop.

Brody is second in line.

There are four people between Brody and Kirstie.

What is Kirstie's position in the line?

fourth   fifth   sixth   seventh

○   ○   ○   ○

26. Which of the diagrams has one-third of the circles black?

○   ○   ○   ○

27. The temperature at four o'clock was 8 degrees.

It dropped by 3 degrees over the next 2 hours.

What was the temperature at six o'clock?

3 degrees   4 degrees   5 degrees   6 degrees

○   ○   ○   ○

28. These cards are turned over and mixed up.

Jamie-Lee chooses a card at random.

What is the chance that she chooses a heart ♥ ?

○ 1 out of 2   ○ 1 out of 4

○ 2 out of 7   ○ 3 out of 8

29. Wendy made these two spinners.

After she spins the arrows she adds the numbers. The first numbers are 3 + 6 which add to 9.

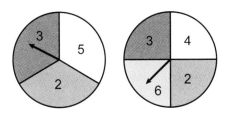

When Wendy spins the arrows again, what total is impossible?

7	8	11	10
○	○	○	○

30. What number is two thousand less than 31 375?

Write your answer in the box.

31. Here are four pies.

A group of boys eat half a pie each.

If all the pies are eaten, how many boys are in the group?

2	4	6	8
○	○	○	○

32. A large club has 50 soccer players in their under 10s teams.

If each team has 12 or 13 players, how many under 10s teams are there in the club?

3	4	5	6
○	○	○	○

33. This is a plan of part of a shopping mall.

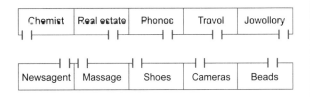

Laura left the Phone shop and turned left.

What is the second shop on her right?

○ Chemist   ○ Newsagent

○ Jewellery   ○ Beads

34. Here are the first four numbers in a pattern. Which of these is the rule used in the pattern?

2	5	14	41

○ Add 3.

○ Multiply by 3 and then subtract 1.

○ Multiply by 2 and then add 1.

○ Divide by 2 and then add 4.

35. Joachim has a piano lesson starting at quarter past four.

This digital clock shows the present time.

3:53

How many minutes before his lesson starts?

○ 22 minutes   ○ 8 minutes

○ 32 minutes   ○ 18 minutes

36. Batteries are sold in packets of four.

Joanna needs 14 batteries.

How many packets does she need to buy?

packets

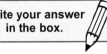

Write your answer in the box.

☞ Answers and explanations on page 159

37. A fruit shop has too many bananas.

It gives away 3 bananas with every bag of oranges sold.

If 32 bags of oranges are sold, how many bananas were given away?

[ ] bananas

Write your answer in the box.

38. The population of Arusha was 4870.

Five years later the population has increased by 310. What is the new population?

7970	4901	5171	5180
○	○	○	○

39. Garth and Gavin had a sheet of stickers each.

Garth's stickers   Gavin's stickers

Garth used half of his heart stickers and Gavin used a third of his smiley stickers.

What is the total number of stickers remaining?

[ ] stickers

Write your answer in the box.

40. The sector graph shows the way 36 students travel to school.

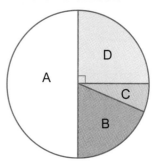

It is known that:

- more students catch the bus than walk to school
- 18 students travel to school in a car
- a quarter of the students ride to school.

Which section of the graph represents the students who catch the bus?

A	B	C	D
○	○	○	○

END OF TEST

Well done! You have completed the third Numeracy Test. We tried to change the questions and some were a little harder. Don't worry if you didn't finish it in time as we added some new types of questions.

How did you go with these test questions? Check to see where you did well and where you had problems. Try to revise the questions that were hard for you.

Use the diagnostic chart on pages 47–48 to see which level of ability you reached. This is only an estimate. Don't be surprised if you answered some difficult questions correctly or even missed some easier questions.

There is now one last practice test that contains 40 questions.

Instructions

- As you check the answer for each question, mark it as correct (✓) or incorrect (✗). Mark any questions that you omitted or left out as incorrect (✗) for the moment.
- Then look at how many you answered correctly in each level.
- You will be able to see what level you are at by finding the point where you started having consistent difficulty with questions. For example, if you answered most questions correctly up to the Intermediate level and then got most questions wrong from then onwards, it is likely your ability is at an Intermediate level. You can ask your parents or your teacher to help you do this if it isn't clear to you.

Am I able to ...

	SKILL	ESTIMATED LEVEL	✓ or ✗
1	Interpret data in a table to solve an addition problem?	Basic	
2	Solve a money problem involving subtraction?	Basic	
3	Identify all lines of symmetry in a shape?	Basic	
4	Identify a specific date on a calendar?	Basic	
5	Recognise a common 2D shape?	Basic	
6	Measure area by counting whole squares?	Basic	
7	Recognise a common 3D shape?	Basic	
8	Use problem-solving strategies to complete number sentences?	Basic	
9	Solve a problem involving rounding?	Basic	
10	Solve a problem involving division?	Basic	
11	Use addition to find the sum of five numbers less than 10?	Basic	
12	Identify angles which measure less than 90 degrees?	Intermediate	
13	Recognise all factors of a number?	Intermediate	
14	Interpret data from column graphs to confirm a statement?	Intermediate	
15	Uses problem-solving strategies to complete number sentences with multiple operations?	Intermediate	
16	Use clues to find a number?	Intermediate	
17	Apply knowledge of place value to six-digit numbers?	Intermediate	
18	Check for correct use of inequalities in number sentences?	Intermediate	
19	Interpret data in a table to make conclusions?	Intermediate	
20	Compare the properties of 3D shapes?	Intermediate	
21	Apply strategies such as multiplication to solve a word problem?	Intermediate	
22	Use strategies to solve problems involving measurement?	Intermediate	
23	Apply strategies to problems involving addition and subtraction?	Intermediate	
24	Use strategies to subtract two- and three-digit numbers?	Intermediate	

	SKILL	ESTIMATED LEVEL	✓ or ✗
25	Use strategies to solve a word problem?	Advanced	
26	Match shading of an object with the correct fraction?	Advanced	
27	Use strategies to solve a word problem?	Advanced	
28	Describe probability using numerical values?	Advanced	
29	Use strategies to solve problems involving addition?	Advanced	
30	Use strategies to subtract from a five-digit number?	Advanced	
31	Solve a problem involving fractions?	Advanced	
32	Solve a problem involving division with a remainder?	Advanced	
33	Interpret a map and follow directions to locate a position?	Advanced	
34	Determine the rule used in a number pattern involving two steps?	Advanced	
35	Solve a word problem using analog and digital time?	Advanced	
36	Solve a problem involving division?	Advanced	
37	Solve a problem involving multiplication?	Advanced	
38	Apply addition strategies to solve a word problem?	Advanced	
39	Solve a problem involving a fraction as an operator?	Advanced	
40	Interpret a sector graph?	Advanced	

NUMERACY TEST 4

This is the fourth Numeracy Test. There are 40 questions.

If you aren't sure what to do, ask your teacher or your parents to help you. Don't be afraid to ask if it isn't clear to you.

These questions will be harder than the earlier Numeracy Tests so don't worry if you can't answer all the questions. Allow around 50 minutes for this test.

Write the answer in the box or colour in the circle with the correct answer. Colour in only one circle for each answer.

1. A week has 7 days.

Which number sentence shows the number of weeks in 14 days?

○ $14 \div 7 = 2$ ○ $14 + 3 = 17$

○ $14 - 3 = 11$ ○ $14 \times 2 = 28$

2. Which of these shapes has two pairs of parallel lines?

circle   triangle   rectangle   pentagon

○   ○   ○   ○

3. The graph shows the favourite sports of a group of students.

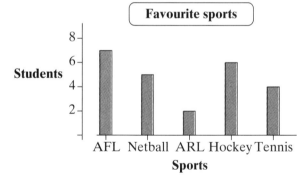

Favourite sports

How many students liked Netball or Hockey?

 Write your answer in the box.

4. Which of these is true?

○ $16 - 8 > 15$ ○ $10 + 4^2 < 20$

○ $6 \div 2 > 7$ ○ $18 \div 2 < 13$

5. A supermarket is selling avocados for $1.49 each.

What is the most number of avocados that can be bought for $5.00?

1	2	3	4
○	○	○	○

6. The table shows the number of movies watched by a group of friends during the holidays.

Name	Number of movies
Gretel	3
Kim	1
Marnee	5
Heidi	3
Lorri	6

How many more movies did Marnee watch than Kim?

4	3	2	1
○	○	○	○

7. There are four shaded shapes below.

Which does **not** have an area of 12 square units?

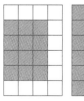

○   ○   ○   ○

49

☞ Answers and explanations on page 159

8. These cards are turned over and mixed up.

9 5 6 7 3 1

A card is selected at random.

What is the chance that the card is odd?

○ certain   ○ very likely

○ very unlikely   ○ impossible

9. Lachlan made up a pattern of numbers.

He started with the number 5 and counted forward by 4.

Which is Lachlan's pattern?

○ 5, 4, 3, 2, …   ○ 5, 6, 7, 8, …

○ 4, 9, 14, 19, …   ○ 5, 9, 13, 17, …

10. Marion folds a piece of paper in half and cuts out an arrow.

What does the paper look like when she unfolds it?

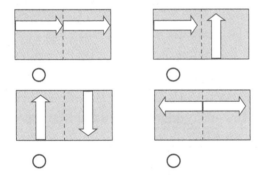

○   ○

○   ○

11. Four girls counted the number of Christmas cards they had handed out and the number of cards they had received.

Name	Handed out	Received
Lori	12	6
Krystal	8	9
Ffion	11	10
Jaylee	14	9

How many Christmas cards were received by the girls?

45   34   18   79

○   ○   ○   ○

12. $54 - 17 =$

Write your answer in the box.

13. Here is the net of a solid.

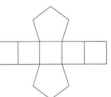

What is the name of the solid formed?

○ pentagonal prism   ○ hexagonal prism

○ octagonal prism   ○ cube

14. Goran drew some shapes on a sheet of paper.

He then rotated the sheet of paper.

Which of these **cannot** be his sheet?

○   ○   ○   ○

15. This picture shows a camera's memory card alongside a ruler.

What is the length of the memory card in millimetres?

mm

Write your answer in the box.

16. Daniela drew this shape.

How many axes of symmetry does her shape have?

0	1	2	4
○	○	○	○

17. Bob is parked on a straight road between Kanga Gully and Elders Bridge near this sign.

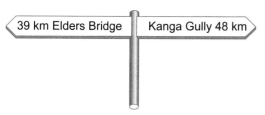

39 km Elders Bridge   Kanga Gully 48 km

What is the distance between Kanga Gully and Elders Bridge?

☐ km

Write your answer in the box.

18. The map shows the homes of school friends in a town.

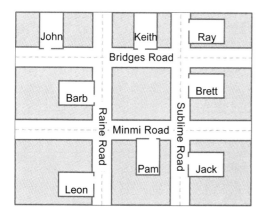

Keith leaves his home and turns left.

He turns right at the next street.

Whose house does he pass by next?

Leon	Ray	Brett	Barb
○	○	○	○

19. The diagram below shows four cans containing black balls and white balls. Lori takes one ball from a can without looking.

Which can gives the **best chance** of choosing a black ball?

○	○	○	○

20. 6.87 is equal to

○ 6 + 0.8 + 0.07

○ 6 + 0.8 + 0.7

○ 0.6 + 0.8 + 0.7

○ 6 + 0.08 + 0.07

21. Which of these times is 5 minutes before eleven o'clock?

10:55	11:05	11:11	10:11
○	○	○	○

22. There are two missing numbers in this number sentence.

| 3 | ? | 2 | + | 6 | 5 | = | 4 | 3 | ? |

The numbers are

☐ and ☐

Write your answer in the boxes.

23. A bag contains eight numbered cards.

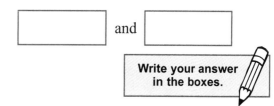

Two cards are chosen to make a number.

Which of these numbers is it impossible to make?

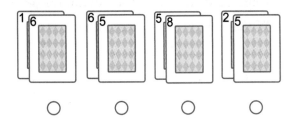

○   ○   ○   ○

---

24. Mrs Folkes buys Easter Buns in packets of 6.

If she needs 27 buns, how many packets will she have to buy?

    4   5   6   8

    ○   ○   ○   ○

---

25. Daniel is saving money to buy a refrigerator that costs $960.

He has already saved $810.

How much more does he have to save?

   $150 $170 $250 $270

    ○   ○   ○   ○

---

26. Mary has this card.

Peter has these five cards.

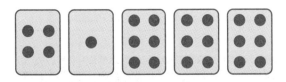

Mary closes her eyes and Peter mixes his cards.

If Mary picks one of Peter's cards, what is the chance that it will match her card?

impossible   unlikely   very likely   certain

    ○   ○   ○   ○

---

27. The diagram shows a petrol gauge.

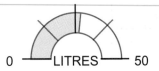

About how many litres of petrol are in the tank?

  27 litres   22 litres   32 litres   2 litres

    ○   ○   ○   ○

---

28. Micah buys a packet of pumpkin seeds.

He puts 3 seeds in each of his pots.

He uses 6 pots and has 2 seeds left over.

How many seeds were in the packet at the start?

    7   11   16   20

    ○   ○   ○   ○

29.

Lionel has crossed out the factors of 16.

He then crosses out the factors of 18 and the factors of 20.

How many numbers will have been crossed out in total?

[   ]   **Write your answer in the box.**

---

30. 6 children share 3 apples equally.

What part of an apple will each child receive?

  $\frac{1}{2}$ $\frac{1}{3}$ $\frac{1}{4}$ $\frac{1}{6}$

    ○   ○   ○   ○

31.

What are the missing numbers?

[ ] and [ ]

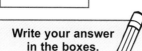

Write your answer in the boxes.

32. What fraction of the shape is shaded?

- ○ one-third
- ○ three-eighths
- ○ three-quarters
- ○ three-fifths

33. If $17 \times 8 = 136$, then $17 \times 80 =$

[ ]

Write your answer in the box.

34. In the diagram, Rick has drawn three shapes and written the numbers from 1 to 12.

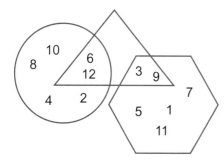

Even numbers have been written inside the circle and odd numbers written inside the hexagon.

There are two numbers inside both the circle and the triangle.

If Rick had written the numbers from 1 to 20 in the diagram, how many numbers would be inside the circle but not inside the triangle?

4	5	6	7
○	○	○	○

35. Six onions are on sale for $3.00.

6 for $3

How much will Con pay for 24 onions?

$ [ ]

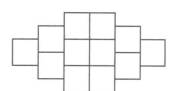

Write your answer in the box.

36. A quarter of the squares in the shape are to be shaded.

How many squares will **not** be shaded?

3	4	8	9
○	○	○	○

37. A group of students wrote their heights on the board.

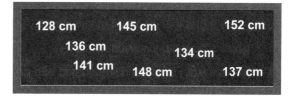

128 cm   145 cm   152 cm
136 cm   134 cm
141 cm   148 cm   137 cm

What is the difference between the tallest student and the shortest student?

8 cm	18 cm	20 cm	24 cm
○	○	○	○

☞ Answers and explanations on page 160

38. A gardener buys bamboo sticks to use in his garden to support his bean plants.

The sticks can only be bought in packets of 10.

3 bamboo sticks are used for each bean plant.

How many packets will he need to buy to support 12 bean plants?

Write your answer in the box.

39. Here is a number line.

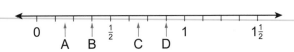

Which letter is pointing to $\frac{7}{8}$?

A   B   C   D

◯   ◯   ◯   ◯

40.

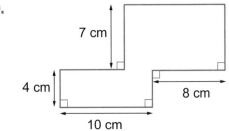

What is the perimeter of the shape?

44 cm   48 cm   50 cm   58 cm

◯   ◯   ◯   ◯

END OF TEST

Well done! You have completed the final Numeracy Test. It means that you have answered or attempted 150 Numeracy questions.

How did you go with these test questions? Check to see where you did well and where you had problems. Try to revise the questions that were hard for you.

Use the diagnostic chart on pages 55–56 to see which level of ability you reached. This is only an estimate. Don't be surprised if you answered some difficult questions correctly or even missed some easier questions.

This is the last Numeracy Test. We will start to look at Literacy tasks in the sections that follow. Now take a well-earned rest.

☞ Answers and explanations on page 161

CHECK YOUR SKILLS: NUMERACY TEST 4

Instructions

- As you check the answer for each question, mark it as correct (✓) or incorrect (✗). Mark any questions that you omitted or left out as incorrect (✗) for the moment.
- Then look at how many you answered correctly in each level.
- You will be able to see what level you are at by finding the point where you started having consistent difficulty with questions. For example, if you answered most questions correctly up to the Intermediate level and then got most questions wrong from then onwards, it is likely your ability is at an Intermediate level. You can ask your parents or your teacher to help you do this if it isn't clear to you.

Am I able to ...

	SKILL	ESTIMATED LEVEL	✓ or ✗
1	Develop a number sentence using information?	Basic	
2	Recognise parallel lines on 2D shapes?	Basic	
3	Make conclusions by interpreting a column graph?	Basic	
4	Check the accuracy of a number sentence involving an inequality?	Basic	
5	Use rounding methods and multiplication to solve a problem?	Basic	
6	Interpret data in a table?	Basic	
7	Measure area by counting whole- and half-grid squares?	Basic	
8	Use chance terms to describe the outcome in a simple experiment?	Basic	
9	Form a number pattern using a stated rule?	Basic	
10	Visualise the symmetry of a folded shape?	Basic	
11	Interpret data in two-way tables?	Basic	
12	Use subtraction strategies involving two-digit numbers?	Intermediate	
13	Recognise the net of a particular solid?	Intermediate	
14	Select the correct shape after a rotation of an object?	Intermediate	
15	Measure the length of an object?	Intermediate	
16	Identify all lines of symmetry in a design?	Intermediate	
17	Use addition to solve a word problem?	Intermediate	
18	Interpret a map and follow directions to locate a position?	Intermediate	
19	Determine the most likely outcome of simple experiments?	Intermediate	
20	Use place value to compare decimals?	Intermediate	
21	Solve a problem involving time expressed in digital form?	Intermediate	
22	Solve a problem by applying knowledge of place value and addition?	Intermediate	
23	Determine the chance of an event in a simple experiment?	Intermediate	
24	Solve a word problem involving division?	Intermediate	

	SKILL	ESTIMATED LEVEL	✓ or ✗
25	Apply strategies to solve a word problem involving subtraction of three-digit numbers?	Advanced	
26	Use words to describe likelihood in a word problem involving chance?	Advanced	
27	Interpret a diagram to solve a problem?	Advanced	
28	Use problem-solving strategies to complete number sentences with multiple operations?	Advanced	
29	Identify the factors of numbers less than or equal to 20?	Advanced	
30	Solve a problem involving fractions?	Advanced	
31	Solve a problem by applying knowledge of place value and subtraction?	Advanced	
32	Identify a fraction to represent part of a shape?	Advanced	
33	Use place value and multiplication to complete a number sentence?	Advanced	
34	Interpret a diagram using factors and multiples?	Advanced	
35	Solve a word problem using multiplication and division?	Advanced	
36	Shade a fraction of an object?	Advanced	
37	Apply place value strategies to order three-digit numbers?	Advanced	
38	Use a variety of strategies to solve a word problem?	Advanced	
39	Identify the position of a fraction on a number line?	Advanced	
40	Calculate the perimeter of a composite rectangular shape?	Advanced	

This is the first Reading Test. There are 35 questions.

If you aren't sure what to do, ask your teacher or your parents to help you. Don't be afraid to ask if it isn't clear to you.

Allow around 50 minutes for this test. Take a short break if necessary.

In this test you will need to look at a picture or read something first. Then read each question and colour in the circle with the correct answer. Sometimes you will instead have to write an answer in a space provided.

Read *Nodding greenhood orchids* and answer questions 1 to 6.

Nodding greenhood orchids

Not many plants have green flowers. The Australian small greenhood orchid is one that does. There are a number of other Australian plants that have greenish flowers,
5 including a few bottlebrushes, some gums and a couple of types of kangaroo paws.

The greenhood orchid is an odd little plant. It has a stem about 40 centimetres long, which may carry a number of green
10 flowers. The hood-like flowers are about 2 centimetres long. Nodding greenhoods flower in winter to early spring (July to October) and prefer moist sheltered areas

15 in open forests and woodlands on a variety of soils.

The plants often grow in small clumps in the bush. Because greenhoods are small and the flowers look like leaves, they easily go unnoticed in the bush.

20 Many other orchids grow on trees or on damp rocks. Greenhoods can grow in dry sandy soil on rocky ridges, far from the coast.

By the end of spring, the plants die back
25 and wait for the next growing season. They store water in a tuber (a type of bulb). They can survive droughts.

Bees pollinate most flowering plants. Greenhood orchids are pollinated by gnats
30 and by members of the mosquito family.

What will happen to the orchid? The spread of towns and land clearing for farms mean that the places where it grows naturally are disappearing. Stock trample many plants
35 before they can flower.

In the bush wild goats are a threat. Goats eat the young plants, and cause erosion. There are plans to fence off small areas where greenhood orchids grow.

40 Weeds spreading into bushland, such as the so-called asparagus fern, smother ground orchids. It would be a shame if the greenhood orchid were to disappear forever.

READING TEST 1

1. According to the text, which statement is correct?

○ Greenhood orchids in clumps are becoming a menace in the bush.

○ Greenhood orchids rely on bees for pollination.

○ Greenhood orchids are easy to spot in their bush setting.

○ Greenhood orchids keep a supply of water in their root system.

2. Which of the options is **not** a threat to the survival of greenhood orchids?

○ goats

○ farms

○ droughts

○ new houses

3. Which of these options is an opinion and **not** a fact?

○ Greenhood orchids are a green Australian flower.

○ Many orchids grow on rocks or in trees.

○ It would be a shame if greenhood orchids become extinct.

○ Greenhood orchids can survive periods of dry weather.

4. The writer describes asparagus fern as a *so-called* fern. What is the most likely reason for using this term?

○ The plant called asparagus fern is a weed.

○ No one is really sure of its correct name.

○ Asparagus fern smothers other small plants.

○ The plant called asparagus fern is not a fern.

5. What is the most likely reason greenhood orchids nod?

○ The flowers are too heavy for the 40-centimetre stem.

○ A breeze will make the flowers sway on their long stems.

○ The orchids get tired when flowering.

○ Mosquitoes land on the flowers and make them bend.

6. Why do greenhood orchids often go unnoticed in the bush?

○ Asparagus fern covers them up.

○ The flowers look like green leaves.

○ The orchids grow a long way from the coast.

○ The orchids flower in winter and no one sees them.

Read the text about Alicia and Holly and answer questions 7 to 13.

After Alicia's first day at her new school Holly took her back to the library. 'I can't be a monitor yet, but I'd really like a book to read,' Alicia explained.

5 'But it's close to closing time. There might not be time.'

'You have less than 20 minutes. Then I close the doors,' said Mr Stone without looking up from his computer as the girls entered.

☞ **Answers and explanations on page 161**

10 'Hurry,' urged Holly.

They worked their way past picture book stands, across aisles and around work-stations. Finally they found Junior Fiction.

A bell rang in the distance. 'Hurry,' urged
15 Holly again. 'That's the warning bell.'

As Alicia pulled a book off the shelf other books tumbled to the floor. Holly looked around guiltily.

'Help me!' pleaded Alicia in an urgent
20 whisper. But the more they hurried the more they fumbled around. Alicia pushed some books back onto the shelf.

Holly looked at her. 'They have to be in order or … '

25 Suddenly the lights went off. In the distance the front doors closed with a deep thud. The girls looked at each other. They were locked in Mr Stone's library.

'How do we get out?' hissed Alicia. Holly
30 was wide-eyed.

'Do you remember how to get to the front desk?' asked Alicia urgently.

Holly nodded, then shook her head. 'It could be this way.'

35 Silently they began to make their way through the maze of dim rows and aisles. The shelves were much too high to see over.

'This way, I think. No, we've gone too
40 far towards the centre. We should go back to where we were and start again,' said Holly. They tried to retrace their steps to Junior Fiction. The deepening gloom made everything look different, strange and
45 spooky. They stopped and looked at each other. They knew they were lost. Lost in The Grange Library.

7. Why was Holly telling Alicia to hurry when they were in the library?
- ○ Mr Stone didn't like children in his library.
- ○ It was getting too dark to see.
- ○ The library was about to close.
- ○ Alicia had dropped some books on the floor.

8. Which term best describes how The Grange Library made the girls feel?
- ○ nervous
- ○ fascinated
- ○ ashamed
- ○ embarrassed

9. How did Alicia feel when she realised the library had closed?
- ○ bold
- ○ panicky
- ○ sure of herself
- ○ relaxed

10. Write the numbers 1 to 4 in the boxes to show the order of the following events in this story.

☐	The girls entered the library to get a book for Alicia.
☐	Alicia knocked some books off the shelf.
☐	The warning bell rang.
☐	The library lights went off.

11. Holly didn't answer Alicia's question: *How do we get out?* This shows that Holly
- ○ thought it was a silly question.
- ○ was not confident she knew the answer.
- ○ didn't want to make a noise in the library.
- ○ had no idea what Alicia was talking about.

12. What was the main reason Holly went with Alicia to the library?

○ so Alicia would not be afraid of Mr Stone

○ She was helping Alicia because it was her first day at the school.

○ to show Alicia how to become a library monitor

○ The library shelves were too high for Alicia to see over.

13. You read that *Holly looked around guiltily.* Why did Holly feel guilty?

○ Alicia was behaving badly.

○ They were in the wrong section of the library.

○ Holly didn't know where the front door was.

○ They might have upset Mr Stone by spilling his books.

Read the text and look at the *Earth Day* poster and answer questions 14 to 18.

Earth Day

Earth Day

7 easy ways to make EVERY DAY Earth Day

Read a library book

Take a litterless lunch

Make craft objects out of used things

Ride your bike or your scooter

Trade stuff — or give it away

Remember to turn off lights

Even children can save energy and help make the Earth a better place for the next generation. Do your bit! It all counts.

NO JUNK MAIL

Make a NO JUNK MAIL sign for your letterbox

Earth Day, 22 April, began in 1970. It is a global day for people to think about protecting the earth. It is a day that inspires awareness of the Earth's natural environment. Many schools support Earth Day activities. The aim in schools is to raise awareness about energy and make savings in energy used in schools.

This poster on Peter's classroom door shows simple ways students can make a difference.

☞ **Answers and explanations on page 162**

14. The seven listed activities are easy to do

○ and don't cost the student any money.

○ but require the help of an adult.

○ and are best done with friends.

○ but are not very sensible.

15. Making craft objects out of used material is a

○ waste of time.

○ way to prevent crime.

○ very costly activity.

○ type of recycling.

16. Turning off lights is very important because it saves

○ housekeeping money.

○ time.

○ energy.

○ family disputes.

17. Of the seven activities, which would be the simplest and easiest to do?
Write your answer on the line.

_____

18. Earth Day is called a *global day*. This means it

○ only happens in the daytime.

○ comes around once every year.

○ has been a special day since 1970.

○ is a day for the whole world to observe.

Read *Health Day at school* and answer questions 19 to 23.

Health Day at school

Last Friday we had a Health Day at school. We didn't do real lessons but had activities most of the day to show the students how to live healthy, happy lives.

5 We started the morning with a yoga and meditation session. Mr Goward runs classes at the sports club. He said all that is needed to do yoga is a desire to be happy. Yoga is a combination of breathing exercises,
10 physical postures and meditation that has been practised for more than 5000 years in India. It is a way of keeping fit and healthy. The yoga class lasted for about half an hour. It was quite relaxing but I got a bit
15 restless towards the end.

After that, Mr Fuller led the group in a walk around the nature reserve behind the school. We weren't allowed to run or talk too loudly. About halfway around
20 we stopped and did some deep breathing exercises. Mr Fuller asked if we could smell the bush. We could! I've never noticed that before.

☞ **Answers and explanations on page 162**

On our return we sat on the grass under a
₂₅ tree. Ms Chan gave us a talk on preventing
skin cancer. I knew most of what she told us
but it was good to be reminded. I sometimes
get too lazy to wear my hat when I go out in
the sun. I'll have to do better.

₃₀ After recess we watched a video about
smoking and lung cancer. Some of the
things that go into cigarettes are disgusting.
Worse than that were the pictures of what
cancer does to the human body. Why
₃₅ people smoke I'll never know!

The next activity was fun. We were shown
how to make healthy fruit drinks—then we
were allowed to make our own. There were
boxes of different fruit we could choose
₄₀ from. Most people picked oranges but I
made a mixture of orange and apple. We
could add water but we were not allowed to
add any sugar.

After lunch we had a short talk from
₄₅ Mr Ireland about being good sportspeople
then we were split into groups to do Olympic
activities. I prefer individual activities to
team games but it was interesting trying out
something you have never done before.

19. This passage could best be described as

○ a narrative.

○ a recount.

○ a description.

○ an explanation.

20. The main purpose of the yoga session was to

○ provide mental and physical relaxation.

○ prepare the students for a difficult walk.

○ fill in time before Mr Fuller arrived.

○ show students how to improve posture.

21. Which Health Day activity did the narrator enjoy the most?

○ yoga

○ bushwalking

○ skin cancer talk

○ making a healthy fruit drink

22. Which activity did the narrator find most upsetting?

○ Mr Ireland's talk

○ the smoking video

○ Ms Chan's talk

○ the meditation session

23. What would be an alternative suitable title for the passage?

○ Fun at school

○ School visitors

○ Healthy lifestyle

○ A day without lessons

Read *Arrest that cat* and answer
questions 24 to 28.

Arrest that cat

It isn't very hard to rhyme
A cat-a-logue of feline crime.

The scratches on the polished floor;
A hole torn in the new screen door;

☞ **Answers and explanations on page 163**

_5_ The cat-er-wauling through the night
That wakes the neighbour's dogs in fright;

A goldfish dead upon the floor
Scooped from its tank by someone's paw;

Mum's broken vase and scattered flowers
_10_ The list goes on for hours and hours

An extra-special meal of fish—
Smoked salmon—stolen from the dish

The cat flap swinging in the door
With footprints from a muddy paw

_15_ A cat-a-strophic tale of woe
Caused by our cat Geronimo

Elaine Horsfield

24. The term _cat-er-wauling_ refers to a

○ serious crime.

○ loud cry.

○ cat and dog fight.

○ scratching sound.

25. Geronimo could best be described as

○ lazy.

○ cunning.

○ secretive.

○ badly behaved.

26. The poem is called _Arrest that cat!_ Why?

○ The cat cannot pay for the damage it has caused.

○ The cat is doing things that endanger the poet's life.

○ The poet feels something drastic has to be done.

○ The poet doesn't like cats.

27. Write the line from the poem that tells readers that the crimes listed are not the full list.

_____

28. The poet has used several words that contain the word _cat_. This is mostly meant to

○ show how unhappy the poet really feels.

○ keep the poem cheerful and amusing.

○ upset people who have cats as pets.

○ give readers a warning about cat problems.

Read _Instructions for using an inhaler_ and answer questions 29 to 35.

Instructions for using an inhaler

Inhalers are used by people to treat or control breathing complaints, such as asthma.

When you inhale a dose you are breathing in the actual dose size required. Aerosol _5_ sprays do not have the same precise control of the dosage. Most inhalers produce a powdered medicine which you will not feel or taste as you inhale.

Your inhaler may be equipped with a dose _10_ indicator. This will indicate the number of doses left in the inhaler.

If you follow these instructions, most inhalers are simple to use:

_15_ **1. Remove the cap.**

☞ **Answers and explanations on pages 163–164**

2. Twist the grip to the right, then the left.

Hold the inhaler upright and turn the grip to the right as far as it will go. Then twist the grip back again (to the left) until it clicks.

The inhaler is now loaded with a measured dose.

Dosage indicator

3. Breathe in.

After breathing out gently, put the mouthpiece between your lips and breathe in deeply through your mouth.

4. Replace the cap and screw it shut.

The mouthpiece should be cleaned with a tissue two or three times a week.

Do not wash the mouthpiece.

29. This type of inhaler is mainly designed for

○ emergency situations.

○ use after being washed.

○ ease of cleaning.

○ safe use.

30. These instructions would most likely be available in a

○ chemist shop.

○ sports club dressing room.

○ school canteen.

○ dentist's surgery.

31. Which word in the text could be replaced with the word *Directions*.

Write your answer on the line.

_____

32. What disadvantage is there in using an aerosol applicator?

○ They are too large for young children.

○ They don't give an exact dosage of the medicine.

○ They are difficult to clean.

○ They only work with powdered medicines.

33. After the cap is removed, the inhaler should be

○ turned upside down.

○ shaken rapidly.

○ twisted to the right.

○ twisted to the left.

☞ Answers and explanations on page 164

34. The inhaler is ready for use

- ○ once the cap is removed.
- ○ after it is put into the mouth.
- ○ as soon as it is washed.
- ○ when it clicks after being twisted.

35. The inhaler delivers a *measured dose*. This means

- ○ the dosage size is controlled by the user.
- ○ it is always the same exact amount.
- ○ it is a numbered dose as shown by the indicator.
- ○ no two doses are exactly the same.

END OF TEST

Well done! You have completed the first Reading Test. This test had different types of questions. They were like comprehension passages. You had to look at something or read something then make a judgement.

In the NAPLAN Tests all the reading matter is in a separate booklet. Don't try to read all of the booklet before answering the questions. It may take too long to read everything. Look at the booklet quickly. Read each section when you come to answer the questions for it.

How did you find these questions? We hope that you found them interesting. Revise anything that was hard for you. There are further questions in the next Reading Test. The next test contains some different questions. Take a long break before doing any more tests.

Use the diagnostic chart on page 66 to see which level of ability you reached. This is only an estimate. Don't be surprised if you answered some difficult questions correctly or even missed some easier questions.

Please note that multiple interpretations are possible for the levels of difficulty of these tasks. Also, some questions involve skills from different levels. This is only an initial guide to the approximate level of the reading skill assessed.

☞ **Answers and explanations on page 164**

Instructions

- As you check the answer for each question, mark it as correct (✓) or incorrect (✗). Mark any questions that you omitted or left out as incorrect (✗) for the moment.
- Then look at how many you answered correctly in each level.
- You will be able to see what level you are at by finding the point where you started having consistent difficulty with questions. For example, if you answered most questions correctly up to the Intermediate level and then got most questions wrong from then onwards, it is likely your ability is at an Intermediate level. You can ask your parents or teacher to help you do this if this is not clear to you.

Am I able to ...

	SKILL	ESTIMATED LEVEL	✓ or ✗
1	Isolate a fact in the text?	Intermediate	
2	Find a fact in the text?	Basic	
3	Distinguish fact from opinion?	Intermediate	
4	Explain an unusual term?	Advanced	
5	Infer a reason?	Advanced	
6	Find a fact in the text?	Basic	
7	Provide a reason for a certain behaviour?	Intermediate	
8	Identify a reaction to a situation?	Intermediate	
9	Infer a reason for a feeling?	Basic	
10	Sequence the order of events?	Intermediate	
11	Infer a reason for a reaction?	Advanced	
12	Isolate a fact in the text?	Basic	
13	Infer a reason for an action?	Advanced	
14	Infer a level of difficulty?	Intermediate	
15	Give a reason for an activity?	Basic	
16	Find indirectly stated information?	Basic	
17	Make a value judgement?	Intermediate	
18	Determine the meaning of a term?	Intermediate	
19	Recognise a text type?	Intermediate	
20	Find a reason for a reaction?	Intermediate	
21	Find a fact not directly stated?	Basic	
22	Infer a feeling?	Basic	
23	Recognise an appropriate title?	Advanced	
24	Determine the meaning of an unusual term from its context?	Advanced	
25	Recognise a character trait?	Intermediate	
26	Appreciate the significance of a title?	Advanced	
27	Identify a relevant section of a poem?	Intermediate	
28	Recognise a poet's intent?	Advanced	
29	Find indirectly stated information?	Intermediate	
30	Infer a reason based upon information and experience?	Intermediate	
31	Recognise a synonym?	Intermediate	
32	Find indirectly stated information?	Advanced	
33	Find directly stated information in the text?	Intermediate	
34	Find directly stated information in the text?	Intermediate	
35	Interpret the meaning of a term from its context?	Advanced	

READING TEST 2

This is the second Reading Test. There are 35 questions.

If you aren't sure what to do, ask your teacher or your parents to help you. Don't be afraid to ask if it is not clear to you.

Allow around 50 minutes for this test. Take a short break if necessary.

In this test you will need to look at a picture or read something first. Then read each question and colour in the circle with the correct answer. Sometimes you will have to write an answer in a space provided.

Look at this advertisement and answer questions 1 to 7.

The Happy Hoot information is from a magazine.

1 A full day's fun for the whole family
2 The Happy Hoot Fun Park is 5 hectares of adventure and fun. It's a great day out for all the family.
3 It's a great place for children's parties and social parties.

4 *Activities include:*
5 two open waterslides   jumbo slide   toddler slide   freefall slide
6 toboggan run   mountain boards   tricycles   swings and see-saws
7 shoot for the basket   half tennis court   beach volleyball   swimming pool
8 trampolines   BMX and mountain bikes speed karts (fully enclosed footwear essential for both activities)
9 mini-golf   nine-hole golf course

10 Also, a well stocked kiosk and souvenir gallery.
11 Plenty of undercover seating with free gas barbecues with shaded picnic areas by the creek.

12 **Charges**
13 *9 years and over: $25 per person per day. CHEAP!*
14 *3 to 8 years: $15 per person per day. CHEAP!*
15 *Children under three years are admitted free to the park,*
16 *with use of swimming pool and limited rides, toddler slide,*
17 *trampoline and swings. Parental supervision required.*

Operating Hours:
Open 10am - 4pm every day.
How to get to the Happy Hoot
Just 45 minutes south of Willang on the Forest Hwy
Follow the BIG Happy Hoot signs.
Coach tours are welcome. Ample parking provided.

READING TEST 2

1. The main purpose of this information is to
   ○ educate people about safe activities.
   ○ advise people what they can watch.
   ○ persuade people to visit Happy Hoot.
   ○ explain to people what Happy Hoot means.

2. The word *Hoot* in this advertisement means
   ○ a loud noise.
   ○ enjoyable excitement.
   ○ a feeling of dislike for something worthless.
   ○ the sound an owl makes.

3. Most of the activities at Happy Hoot are
   ○ entertaining.
   ○ relaxing.
   ○ physical.
   ○ competitive.

4. The creek area is set aside for
   ○ swimming.
   ○ family picnics.
   ○ kiosk purchases.
   ○ mountain bike riding.

5. There is a footwear rule for the
   ○ mini golf.
   ○ souvenir gallery.
   ○ whole of Happy Hoot park.
   ○ speed karts.

6. Parental supervision is required for children
   ○ under three years of age.
   ○ on the open water slides.
   ○ riding mountain bikes.
   ○ at birthday parties.

7. Most people going to Happy Hoot can
   ○ easily walk there.
   ○ take a bus.
   ○ use private cars.
   ○ ride the bicycles provided.

Read the text about the snowman and answer questions 8 to 13.

My snowman was turning pink! I raced through the snow to Jasper's house.

He held his chin in his cupped hand and made a slow 'Hmmmm,' then said, 'Sure he's
5 not blue, you know Crystal, blue with cold?'

'We should see the … patient,' he suggested. I didn't like the word 'patient' but we hotfooted, through the deep snow, back to my yard.

10 The snowman was sitting on a snowdrift, shoulders hunched. He was still pink.

'Let's just give him another layer of snow,' Jasper suddenly suggested. I'm sure I saw a light bulb pop out of his head!

15 We quickly patted snow all over our snowman. He was not thrilled with our idea, squirming all the time. After a few frantic minutes we stood back to admire our work. Our snowman was white again.

☞ Answers and explanations on pages 164–165

20 But it didn't last. Slowly the pink seeped
through. I shook my head. It didn't
make sense.

Our head-hanging snowman wouldn't look
at us. Even Jasper was stumped for an
25 explanation.

The snowman turned slowly towards us.
'Please don't stare at me. I don't like it,'
he begged.

'Don't like it!' I snapped. 'Why?'

30 He didn't answer. Eyes downcast.

'Why?' I asked again in a friendlier manner.

'My cheeks are burning and … ' he
mumbled.

'Burning?' That didn't make sense. I looked
35 across the lawn. It was like Antarctica.
'Burning?' I repeated.

He hesitated before replying, 'I'm so hot
and embarrassed I might melt.'

Jasper and I glanced at one another, then at
40 our snowman.

'I don't have any clothes on,' the snowman
blurted. 'Whoever made me forgot the
clothes!'

Jasper and I glanced guiltily at each
45 another—mouths open. We had to do
something, and quick.

8. What colour did the snowman keep
changing to?

○ pink

○ white

○ green

○ blue

9. The snowman was embarrassed
because he was

○ about to melt

○ going blue.

○ turning pink.

○ naked.

10. Crystal says: *I'm sure I saw a light bulb
pop out of his [Jasper's] head!*

What does she mean by this?

○ Jasper was knocked on his head.

○ Jasper had a bright idea.

○ Jasper was getting confused.

○ Jasper needed a light to think.

11. Jasper and Crystal's feeling of
satisfaction lasted

○ a few frantic minutes after finishing
their task.

○ for no time at all.

○ only while they added snow to the
snowman.

○ for a short while.

12. Which word best describes how the
snowman felt?

○ self-conscious

○ cross

○ humble

○ guilty

13. Write the numbers 1 to 4 in the boxes to
show the order of the following events in
this story.

	Jasper and Crystal pack snow onto the snowman.
	The snowman's cheeks start burning.
	Crystal rushes over to Jasper's house.
	The snowman admits why he feels embarrassed.

Read the book review and answer questions 14 to 19.

BOOK REVIEW
Mouse for a Month

I review many books and only a few I describe as 'un-put-downable'. It's not so much that you can't put down *Mouse for a Month*, as that you lose track of all time. The reader is totally swept up by the weird events. I giggled while reading it, and my children did too.

Mouse for a Month was written by Rho Dent (that can't be real!), illustrated by Lewis Ridge and published in 2011. I would describe it as a junior novel as it is written in chapters but with more white space and larger print than chapter books for older readers. Ridge's quirky sketches add extra humour for those who like comic-type characters. Junior kids will snap it up.

The novel is about a mouse, and would you believe his name is Nicky and his girlfriend is Ninnie! But what a mighty mouse! He is found unexpectedly in Martin's desk at his school. The kids want him to be the class pet and plan to take turns to look after him. It turns out that Nicky has schemes of his own.

To add to the students' problems, the class teacher, Herman Hitails, dislikes rodents of all kinds. He thinks they smell and they make him sneeze.

Martin and his friends have trouble keeping Mr Hitails from discovering why the class is acting strangely. And it's all in the month leading up to the end-of-year school concert.

This book is a great romp. My dislike of small furry things has changed. Who couldn't admire a mouse with the wall-climbing skills of a gecko? Read this book and enjoy Nicky's wild (mis)adventures! I can't wait to read more of Rho Dent's books!

Reviewed by Stephen Trapper in The Book Look *(2011)*

14. After reading the review, anyone buying *Mouse for a Month* would expect a book that was
- ○ thrilling and suspenseful.
- ○ a factual book about caring for mice.
- ○ most suitable for teenage readers.
- ○ full of very comical events.

15. Who provided the illustrations for *Mouse for a Month*?
- ○ Stephen Trapper
- ○ Lewis Ridge
- ○ Rho Dent
- ○ Herman Hitail

16. The reviewer says some books are *un-put-downable*. By this he means the books
- ○ are big and heavy.
- ○ take up a lot of book shelf space.
- ○ keep readers engrossed in the stories.
- ○ are difficult to understand and must be read slowly.

17. How did the reviewer change after reading *Mouse for a Month*?
- ○ He got an attack of the sneezes.
- ○ He decided never to read another Rho Dent book.
- ○ He was not going to write any more reviews.
- ○ He decided mice were pleasant creatures.

18. Nicky is described as having *schemes of his own*. This suggests that Nicky may be

○ mischievous.

○ mysterious.

○ spiteful.

○ timid.

19. What is the main reason the reviewer suggests the book is suitable for younger readers?

○ It is written in chapters.

○ The illustrator is Lewis Ridge.

○ It has large print on uncrowded pages.

○ The subject is a mouse in a classroom.

Read *Antarctica facts* and answer questions 20 to 25.

Antarctica facts

Antarctica is the continent south of Australia. It is sometimes called the South Pole. The whole area is called the Antarctic region.

Antarctica (14 million square kilometres) is almost twice the size of Australia. Less than 2% of the continent is ice-free—it is almost totally covered in ice. The ice is generally 2.5 kilometres deep (2500 metres) but in places it is 5 kilometres deep. Antarctica contains about 70% of the world's fresh water. If the ice melted the world's oceans would rise 70 metres.

If the above is true, why then is Antarctica called the world's driest continent? It is even drier than Australia! The reason is simple—it rarely rains or snows there. The ice has built up over thousands of years. It never melts. Pictures of explorers caught in snowstorms only give part of the truth. It is the windiest place on Earth. Much of the snow and ice is whipped up off the ground by ferocious winds.

If the depth of ice is included then Antarctica has the greatest average height of all the continents. Most of Antarctica is 2.5 kilometres (2500 metres) above sea level. Australia's average elevation is only 340 *metres*. Parts of central Australia are lower than sea level (–15 metres).

Steep mountain slopes are a few of the places that are without ice or snow. The rock is exposed to winds so strong for most of the year that snow or ice cannot take hold.

The Australian Antarctic Territory has the highest point in the icy landscape, but the Russian research station recorded the Earth's lowest temperature. In 1983 the temperature dropped to minus 90°C (–90C°). Australia's coldest night was –20°C.

20. The text about Antarctica could best be called a

○ factual report.

○ personal recount.

○ technical explanation.

○ scientific description.

21. What prevents parts of Antarctica from being covered in snow?

Write your answer on the line.

_____

22. According to the text, which statement is correct?

○ Antarctica has the highest snowfall of any continent.

○ Parts of Antarctica are below sea level.

○ More fresh water is stored in Antarctica than on any other continent.

○ Antarctica is half the size of Australia.

23. How deep is some of the deepest ice in Antarctica?

○ 70 metres

○ 340 metres

○ 2500 metres

○ 5 kilometres

24. Pictures of snowstorms in Antarctica are really pictures of

○ hailstorms.

○ heavy, cold rain.

○ thick mist or fog.

○ ground snow stirred up by wild winds.

25. To survive in Antarctica a person would most need shelter from the cold and

○ a shield from ice.

○ a reliable supply of fresh water.

○ protection from the winds.

○ cover from the mountains.

Read *What is a fairy tale?* and answer questions 26 to 31.

What is a fairy tale?

Sometimes it seems easier to say what isn't one. Often the story is not about fairies. *The Three Little Pigs* and *The Ugly Duckling* are examples.

5 Fairy tales usually have such characters as fairies, goblins, giants, trolls, elves, dragons, witches and wizards, wolves and gnomes—with a sprinkling of magic, spells and enchantment.

10 Often the story will involve far-fetched events. Fairy tales reflect the everyday world, but they aren't realistic; animals talk, giants live on clouds, and the dead spring back to life. They exist in a 'once upon a 15 time' world.

Their characters are often nameless; they represent people—and animals. Wonderful things can happen to anyone, including you and me. Anything is possible. A child can 20 become a bird, a frog a prince, a girl in rags a Queen. Good people generally win through or are rewarded—and everyone lives happily ever after.

The early fairy 25 tales were intended for adults as well as children. The Brothers Grimm 30 wrote them for children. Now they are almost always children's stories. Where 35 do fairy tales come from?

☞ **Answers and explanations on page 166**

People have told stories for as long as there has been someone to tell them. Fairy tales were once part of oral storytelling, which included fables, myths and legends, passed down through the generations.

The Brothers Grimm were the first writers who aimed to collect and preserve the stories in a book (1812). In later editions they edited them to make them more suitable for children. Their tales include *Rapunzel* and *Hansel and Gretel*.

Hans Christian Andersen was a great writer of fairy tales. Some of his stories were based on traditional tales (such as *The Princess and the Pea*), but most were original.

He published his first fairy tales in 1835. Many of his stories are still told today, including *The Little Mermaid* and *The Ugly Duckling*. Many have made it into film.

Source: http://en.wikipedia.org/wiki/Fairy_tale

26. A fairy tale is a type of

○ myth.

○ legend.

○ fantasy.

○ fable.

27. Which statement is a fact and not an opinion?

○ Fairy tales make good films.

○ Fairy tales are better than myths.

○ Fairy tales let people forget their troubles.

○ Fairy tales were not always written down.

28. In fairy tales, characters are most often referred to by

○ their real, full names.

○ a description of their looks or what they are.

○ their titles and their names.

○ the names given to fairies.

29. The Brothers Grimm are important because they

○ wrote many new fairy tales.

○ told fairy tales to adults.

○ wrote fairy tales suitable for children.

○ recorded tales that had been told but not written down.

30. Fairy tales have been around for a long time. How did they begin?

Write your answer on the lines.

_____

_____

_____

_____

31. Most fairy tales give the listener a feeling of

○ grief.

○ hope.

○ dread.

○ importance.

READING TEST 2

Look at the cartoon *Smelly footballer* and answer questions 32 to 35.

32. The doctor's reaction to the footballer's injury suggests

  ○ a lack of concern.

  ○ spiteful intentions.

  ○ a fear of being hurt.

  ○ sympathy for the footballer.

33. The stars in the cartoon are used to show

  ○ that the player's injury occurred at night.

  ○ that the player has head injuries.

  ○ how highly the cartoon is rated.

  ○ who is the most important person.

34. The cartoon is amusing because

  ○ the player is not really hurt.

  ○ football players are really softies.

  ○ the doctor is dressed in medical clothes.

  ○ the doctor is more worried about the smell than the injury.

35. A suitable, amusing caption for the cartoon would be

  ○ The game must go on

  ○ Doctor to the rescue!

  ○ A fake injury

  ○ Sport is dangerous

END OF TEST

Well done! You have completed the second Reading Test. This test had different types of questions. They were like comprehension passages. You had to look at something or read something then make a judgement.

How did you find the questions? We hope you found them interesting. Revise anything that was hard for you. There are further questions in the next Reading Test. The next test contains some different questions. Now take a long break before doing any more tests.

Use the diagnostic chart on page 75 to see which level of ability you reached. This is only an estimate. Don't be surprised if you answered some difficult questions correctly or even missed some easier questions.

Please note that multiple interpretations are possible for the levels of difficulty of these tasks. Also, some questions involve skills from different levels. This is only an initial guide to the approximate level of the reading skill assessed.

☞ Answers and explanations on page 167

Instructions

- As you check the answer for each question, mark it as correct (✓) or incorrect (✗). Mark any questions that you omitted or left out as incorrect (✗) for the moment.
- Then look at how many you answered correctly in each level.
- You will be able to see what level you are at by finding the point where you started having consistent difficulty with questions. For example, if you answered most questions correctly up to the Intermediate level and then got most questions wrong from then onwards, it is likely your ability is at an Intermediate level. You can ask your parents or teacher to help you do this if this is not clear to you.

Am I able to ...

	SKILL	ESTIMATED LEVEL	✓ or ✗
1	Understand the purpose of a text?	Intermediate	
2	Determine the meaning of a word from its context?	Intermediate	
3	Make a generalisation?	Basic	
4	Find a fact?	Basic	
5	Isolate a relevant fact?	Basic	
6	Find a stated fact?	Basic	
7	Infer a fact from given information?	Intermediate	
8	Find a basic fact?	Basic	
9	Infer a reason from an event?	Intermediate	
10	Interpret idiom?	Advanced	
11	Find a fact?	Intermediate	
12	Describe a feeling?	Intermediate	
13	Sequence a series of events in a narrative?	Intermediate	
14	Predict the likelihood of a reaction?	Advanced	
15	Find a stated fact?	Basic	
16	Interpret idiom?	Advanced	
17	Determine cause and effect?	Intermediate	
18	Interpret the meaning of an expression from its context?	Advanced	
19	Explain the reason for an opinion?	Intermediate	
20	Recognise a text type?	Intermediate	
21	Find a reason for a condition?	Advanced	
22	Isolate a relevant fact from the text?	Advanced	
23	Find a stated fact?	Intermediate	
24	Find a fact not directly stated?	Advanced	
25	Predict a rational reaction?	Advanced	
26	Recognise a specific text type?	Advanced	
27	Distinguish between fact and opinion?	Advanced	
28	Find a stated fact?	Intermediate	
29	Find a stated fact?	Intermediate	
30	Find a fact not obviously stated?	Intermediate	
31	Make a generalisation?	Advanced	
32	Interpret the actions of a cartoon character?	Advanced	
33	Appreciate a strategy used by cartoonists?	Advanced	
34	Interpret what constitutes the amusing feature of a cartoon?	Advanced	
35	Recognise a suitable caption?	Advanced	

READING TEST 3

Read *The Grand Hoax* and answer questions 1 to 6.

The Grand Hoax

This information many readers may find upsetting.

There is a possibility that this information may soon be banned. It is from my book
5 *The Grand Hoax* which is not on the shelves of most libraries. Take a look. I wouldn't be at all surprised if it's not even listed on the library computer.

Parents will become stressed if they find
10 that you have read the book. If you have a copy, hide it somewhere safe. You could put it in a plastic bag and hide it in the toilet cistern. No one ever looks in there.

Read on, at the risk of having all those
15 beliefs you hold dear to your pure, little heart shattered. Smashed. Exploded. Devastated. Wiped clean from the memory card in your hard-drive brain. Evaporated in a puff of disbelief. Vanished. Into thin air.
20 All you will have left is a vacuum where you once thought you held solid, reliable information. That grey matter of yours is caught up in the hoax. It is being used against you.

25 Your life has been one long confidence trick. Hard to accept, but true, true, true!

Let me explain. It all started with … Let's say, it started with the tooth fairy.

There are people (you can guess who) who
30 want you to believe that a fairy, no larger than a finger and lighter than a feather, flies around at night, in the pitch black, plonking coins into glasses of fresh water. Any fairy would be crushed by a dollar coin. Imagine
35 what a fifty-cent piece could do!

What about slimy frogs that turn into handsome princes when they are kissed by a girl?

What about that Easter rabbit? What
40 about him? The one with chocolate on his buckteeth. Or is it a her? A buck or a doe? Maybe, even a kitten.

Of course, if you are naughty the bogyman will get you. Need I go on?

1. What started with the fairies?

   ○ children losing their teeth
   ○ fairies getting hurt
   ○ putting money in water
   ○ lies told by parents

2. The writer states: *There are people (you can guess who).*

   Who are the people the writer is most likely referring to?

   ○ parents
   ○ deceitful librarians
   ○ handsome princes
   ○ people who swindle other people

3. Where can you find the information that reveals the truth?

   ○ at the library
   ○ on a computer
   ○ in someone's memory
   ○ in a book that might get banned

4. What is the most likely reason the book is called *The Grand Hoax*?

   The book

   ○ reveals made-up stories parents tell their children.
   ○ is not available to children.
   ○ contains information that is not true.
   ○ doesn't actually exist.

5. Why does the writer conclude with: *Need I go on?*

   ○ He doesn't have any more information.
   ○ He thinks he has convinced readers.
   ○ He doesn't want to scare readers.
   ○ He wants readers to get a copy of his book.

6. From the way this text is written, it could be expected that readers will find the information

   ○ very disturbing.
   ○ an amusing explanation.
   ○ an unpleasant surprise.
   ○ a late warning.

Read *Playing with hoops* and answer questions 7 to 12.

Playing with hoops

Hoops have been in use for thousands of years. The ancient Greeks played with them to keep fit and healthy. Greek physicians wrote
5 about hoops as far back as 300 BC.

Hoops were important to Native
10 American boys in target practice games. A screen of plant fibre or rawhide strips was woven into the
15 centre of a wooden hoop. This was bowled along the ground between two rows of players. Players hurled darts at the rapidly rolling hoop. This was good training for when they became hunters.

20 Eskimos played a similar game using poles instead of darts. One person would bowl the hoop along the ground while rival athletes, from two teams, took turns to throw long poles through the hoop. The hoop bowler
25 kept score.

Wooden hoop races for English boys and girls were popular in the 1800s. Hoops were made to suit the contestant's size.

☞ **Answers and explanations on pages 167–168**

They were tapped along with the open hand
30 or a short stick as children raced along
behind them.

In the 1960s a hoop craze swept many
countries. This craze was not for bowling
hoops but for twirling hoops. The hoop,
35 often called a hula-hoop, was a lightweight,
tubular plastic hoop which was twirled
around various parts of the body, especially
the waist. This was the hula-hoop craze.
Schoolchildren were often seen twirling
40 brightly coloured, plastic hoops around
their bodies. Adults played with hula-hoops
too, often hoping to lose weight. Doctors
encouraged hoop activities as exercise. The
Greeks knew this thousands of years earlier!

45 Modern Olympic Games gymnasts
have used hoops, as well
as ribbons and balls, as
props in some gymnastic
events. Gymnastics is
50 one of the most
graceful Olympic
activities.

7. Who used hoops in running races?

○ the ancient Greeks

○ English children

○ Native Americans

○ Olympic gymnasts

8. Hoops were used by Native Americans

○ to keep fit and lose weight.

○ as a fun pastime.

○ to entertain.

○ for training to become a hunter.

9. Hoops have been in use for centuries.
Mostly the reason for their use was

○ practical.

○ educational.

○ medical.

○ private.

10. Hoops were made in different sizes for
races in England. Why?

○ There was no correct size for hoops.

○ The races were not always in the
same place.

○ Different types of wood were used to
make the hoops.

○ They were used by children of different
heights.

11. How were the hoops used in the 1800s
different from those used in the 1960s?

Write your answer on the line.

_____

12. The information in this passage is
generally arranged

○ in order of importance.

○ in the order in which the events
occurred.

○ from the least interesting to the most
interesting.

○ to show how hoops have changed
over time.

☞ Answers and explanations on page 168

Read *Mercury* and answer questions 13 to 18.

Mercury

Mercury is the closest planet to the sun. It is a battered and baked planet slightly larger than the Earth's moon. It is covered in craters. Some craters have ice in them,
5 even though the planet is hot. Sunlight never touches some valley shadows due to the planet's tilt and orbit. Without air, there are huge temperature differences between the coldest and hottest spots. Mercury days
10 are so long that there are big differences between temperatures on the daylight side and the night side.

Mercury was created billions of years ago, when huge rocks collided. After these
15 collisions, the planet was bombarded with meteorites for several hundred million years. There were also many volcanic eruptions. As the planet cooled, the thin, rocky crust shrank in diameter by about
20 3 kilometres.

The Caloris Basin is one of the largest craters on Mercury. This vast crater is 1300 kilometres wide and was formed when a massive rock, about 100 kilometres across,
25 crashed into the surface. The impact created shockwaves across the planet. Beethoven, another large crater, is 643 kilometres across.

The cliffs on Mercury are up to 2 kilometres high, and stretch for hundreds of kilometres.
30 The cliffs were formed when the thin crust crumbled, as volcanic activity slowed down and Mercury became cooler.

One Mercury day lasts about 59 Earth days. Mercury takes about 88 Earth days to have
35 a complete year, instead of the 365 days that we have on Earth. Mercury *rotates* on its axis very slowly but *revolves* around the sun so fast that there are three Mercury days every two Mercury years!

40 Mercury has an odd relationship with the Earth. Every 117 days, when Mercury is closest to Earth, it always has the same side facing us.

Mariner 10 is the only spacecraft to visit
45 Mercury. It made three fly-pasts of Mercury in the 1970s, taking photographs of many cliffs and craters. Although the first series of fly-pasts answered many questions, it has raised others.

Adapted from *Spacescape* by Karl Kruszelnicki, HBJ, 1992
http://www.kidscosmos.org/kid-stuff/mercury-facts.html

13. According to the text, which statement is correct?

○ The Earth is closer to the sun than Mercury.

○ The Earth and Mercury are about the same size.

○ Mercury is an older planet than the Earth.

○ Mercury is about the same size as our moon.

14. How long are days on Mercury compared to Earth days?

- ○ 59 Earth days
- ○ 88 Earth days
- ○ 117 Earth days
- ○ 365 Earth days

15. According to the text, the landform on Mercury is

- ○ plain and flat.
- ○ similar to that on Earth.
- ○ more mountainous than Earth's landform.
- ○ covered with active volcanoes.

16. Mercury has some very cold areas on the surface because of

- ○ its speed around the sun.
- ○ the length of its days.
- ○ its distance from the sun.
- ○ the tilt of the planet.

17. What is the most spectacular feature of Mercury?

- ○ its tilt and orbit
- ○ its volcanoes
- ○ its crumbling crust
- ○ its craters

18. The first close-up photographs of Mercury answered many scientific questions, but, *it has raised others*. By this the writer means

- ○ the photographs showed things scientists don't understand.
- ○ some photographs were not very clear.
- ○ most of Mercury was not photographed.
- ○ the mission to Mercury was unsuccessful.

Read *What is a windsock?* and answer questions 19 to 23.

What is a windsock?

Raincoats keep people dry when it rains but what are windsocks? Are they something you wear on your feet when it's windy?

Windsocks (or wind cones) are weather
5 instruments. They are used to show wind direction and wind speed. They are made from sturdy, light material and look a bit like an ice-cream cone with the small end cut off. The wind can blow straight through.
10 Some people say they look like socks with a big hole in the toe.

Windsocks can be seen at airports on high poles. They let pilots know about the wind as they land or take off. At night they are
15 lit up. There are countries, such as Canada, where the colour of an airstrip's windsock provides information to aircraft pilots. A two-coloured windsock is usually used on licensed runways, whereas a solid
20 orange windsock is usually displayed on unlicensed runways.

Windsocks are also seen along windy parts of roads or on high bridges. They warn drivers, especially drivers of trucks and
25 vans, or drivers pulling caravans, that they have to be careful.

When the wind is strong, windsocks stick straight out. In a light breeze windsocks become limp and droopy and hang down at an angle.

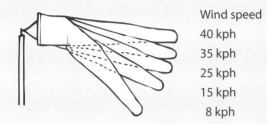

	Wind speed
	40 kph
	35 kph
	25 kph
	15 kph
	8 kph

The direction of the wind is the opposite to the direction the windsock is pointing. If the wind is coming from the south, then the windsock points to the north.

Windsocks were used by the Japanese as kites long before there were aeroplanes. Many were made to look like colourful fish with their mouths open. Streamers were attached to the tail end.

Windsocks are used all over the world—from bases at the South Pole to tropical islands. There is even one on Mars!

19. A windsock is
   ○ an item of clothing.
   ○ a weather predictor.
   ○ a decoration.
   ○ a weather implement.

20. Windsocks have a hole in the pointy end to
   ○ keep them lightweight.
   ○ provide a spot to tie on streamers.
   ○ stop them from becoming limp and droopy.
   ○ let the wind blow through.

21. Windsocks would be of little use
   ○ at an airport.
   ○ on high road bridges.
   ○ at a railway station.
   ○ on a golf course.

22. The angle a windsock makes with the ground indicates
   ○ a safe driving direction.
   ○ the speed of the wind.
   ○ when the wind will change.
   ○ the best time to fly kites.

23. Windsocks have no value at night unless
   ○ they are lit up.
   ○ there is a wind.
   ○ they are brightly coloured.
   ○ they are close to airports.

Read the lyrics of the song *Puff the Magic Dragon* made popular by a trio called Peter, Paul and Mary, and answer questions 24 to 28.

Puff the Magic Dragon

Puff, the magic dragon, lived by the sea

And frolicked in the autumn mist in a land called Honah Lee,

Little Jackie Paper loved that rascal Puff,

And brought him strings and sealing wax and other fancy stuff. Oh

Chorus

Puff, the magic dragon, lived by the sea

And frolicked in the autumn mist in a land
10   called Honah Lee,

Puff, the magic dragon, lived by the sea

And frolicked in the autumn mist in a land
     called Honah Lee.

Together they would travel on a boat with
15   billowed sail

Jackie kept a lookout perched on Puff's
     gigantic tail,

Noble kings and princes would bow
     whene'er they came,

20 Pirate ships would lower their flags when
     Puff roared out his name. Oh!

Chorus

A dragon lives forever but not so little boys

Painted wings and giants' rings make way
25   for other toys.

One grey night it happened, Jackie Paper
     came no more

And Puff, that mighty dragon, he ceased his
     fearless roar.

30 His head was bent in sorrow, green scales
     fell like rain,

Puff no longer went to play along the
     cherry lane.

Without his lifelong friend, Puff could not
35   be brave,

So Puff, that mighty dragon, sadly slipped
     into his cave. Oh!

Chorus

Written by Peter Yarrow and Leonard Lipton, © 1963
Pepamar Music Corp.

---

24. What colour was Puff, the magic dragon?

- ○ grey
- ○ green
- ○ orange
- ○ black

25. What sort of dragon was Puff before Jackie Paper left him?

- ○ fierce
- ○ timid
- ○ gracious
- ○ cheerful

26. Puff could best be described as

- ○ a lifelong companion.
- ○ a spoilt playmate.
- ○ an imaginary friend.
- ○ a cuddly toy.

27. An important idea in the song is that

- ○ dragons can't be trusted.
- ○ childhood doesn't last forever.
- ○ dragons aren't really dangerous.
- ○ boys' games are fun games.

28. You are told: *Jackie Paper came no more.*
What does this line suggest?
Jackie Paper

- ○ was killed by the dragon.
- ○ disappeared into a cave.
- ○ was taken by pirates.
- ○ got older and found new interests.

Read *The agreement* and answer
questions 29 to 35.

The agreement

'We call this the guesthouse,' smiled Paul
Weeks. 'One of the oldest buildings in
Willang Valley. It's been in the family for
generations. It's been, ahh, modernised, a
5 couple of times. It's a bit primitive but cosy,
with the open fire going. You still want to
rent it?'

Martin nodded.

There was no signed lease. The two men
10 simply shook hands and Paul pulled a jingle
of keys from his pocket. 'You probably
won't need these.'

Michael entered the unlocked cottage and
looked around. The grimy windows faced
15 three different directions and from the
kitchen he could partly see the old wooden
bridge that crossed Rocky Creek. It was less
than 100 metres from the cottage.

The kitchen included two big cupboards, a
20 tired looking fridge, two wooden chairs and
a basic sink cupboard under the window
that looked across the river flats. On a low
bookcase were some old paperbacks and
some older copies of *National Geographic*. A
25 dog-eared telephone book hung over the top
shelf but there was no sign of a telephone.

The stone fireplace was set in an external
wall. Paul had a fire set, ready for lighting.
Suddenly Martin shivered.

30 In one corner there was a small chrome
table. The pattern on the top had almost
worn off. Still, it would be a good desk
once he started writing.

Two narrow doors led to smaller rooms.
35 The one on the right was hardly any larger
than a cubby-hole. It had a musty, unaired
smell. The window had not been opened
in years. The room contained a desk, a
chair and a wooden cabinet. A yellowing
40 power point was beside the desk. The floor
creaked as Michael backed out.

The second room was a very small
bedroom with a single bed hard against
the wall longways. A sad looking bed
45 lamp perched on a milk crate and a rickety
wardrobe took up so much room the
bedroom door couldn't fully open.

Cattle could be heard lowing some way
off. Long shadows were creeping towards
50 the creek. A wave of loneliness swept
over Martin.

29. This text is mainly a

- ○ narrative.
- ○ procedure.
- ○ description.
- ○ factual recount.

30. What is the most likely reason for Paul
suggesting that Martin might not need
the keys?

- ○ The house was in an isolated place.
- ○ The windows didn't open.
- ○ The doors could not be locked.
- ○ There was nothing valuable in the house.

☞ **Answers and explanations on page 170**

31. The house could best be described as

○ comfortable.

○ special.

○ well designed.

○ basic.

32. Why would Paul have said: *It's been, ahh, modernised a couple of times.*

○ He was not sure anything had been done to the house.

○ The modern changes to the house had been important.

○ He was trying to remember exactly what had been done.

○ The house may have had changes but it was not all that modern.

33. The door into the bedroom didn't open fully. Why?
Write your answer on the line.

_____

34. Write the numbers 1 to 4 in the boxes to show the order in which Martin looked at things in the house.

☐ the spare room

☐ the fireplace

☐ the view of the bridge

☐ the kitchen sink

35. What could be the main reason for Martin backing out of the first small room off the kitchen?

○ Something in the room upset him.

○ There was not much light in the room.

○ The floor felt unsafe.

○ It was awkward to turn around.

END OF TEST

Well done! You have completed the third Reading Test. This test had different types of questions. They were like comprehension passages. You had to look at something or read something then make a judgement.

How did you find these test questions? We hope that you found them interesting. There are further questions in the final Reading Test.

Use the diagnostic chart on page 85 to see which level of ability you reached. This is only an estimate. Don't be surprised if you answered some difficult questions correctly or even missed some easier questions.

Please note that multiple interpretations are possible for the levels of difficulty of these tasks. Also, some questions involve skills from different levels. This is only an initial guide to the approximate level of the reading skill assessed. No claim is made that this will be identical to the scores a student will receive in the actual tests, as the assessors will use a complex scoring system to estimate a student's level of ability.

Instructions

- As you check the answer for each question, mark it as correct (✓) or incorrect (✗). Mark any questions that you omitted or left out as incorrect (✗) for the moment.
- Then look at how many you answered correctly in each level.
- You will be able to see what level you are at by finding the point where you started having consistent difficulty with questions. For example, if you answered most questions correctly up to the Intermediate level and then got most questions wrong from then onwards, it is likely your ability is at an Intermediate level. You can ask your parents or teacher to help you do this if this is not clear to you.

Am I able to ...

	SKILL	ESTIMATED LEVEL	✓ or ✗
1	Find a stated fact?	Advanced	
2	Interpret a term in the context of a text?	Intermediate	
3	Find a fact?	Basic	
4	Work out a reason for a title?	Advanced	
5	Understand the point of a rhetorical question?	Advanced	
6	Appreciate a writing style?	Advanced	
7	Find a stated fact?	Basic	
8	Isolate a specific reason?	Intermediate	
9	Determine a reason for an occurrence?	Advanced	
10	Determine the reason for an action?	Basic	
11	Compare situations over time?	Intermediate	
12	Analyse the format of a text?	Advanced	
13	Isolate a fact among non-facts?	Intermediate	
14	Find a stated fact?	Basic	
15	Draw a conclusion?	Advanced	
16	Find a specific fact?	Intermediate	
17	Draw a conclusion?	Intermediate	
18	Indicate the meaning of a phrase from its context?	Intermediate	
19	Find a stated fact?	Intermediate	
20	State a reason?	Basic	
21	Draw a conclusion?	Intermediate	
22	Relate text to a picture?	Intermediate	
23	State a reason?	Intermediate	
24	Identify a fact from the text?	Intermediate	
25	Identify a character trait?	Intermediate	
26	Determine a definition of a relationship?	Advanced	
27	Draw a conclusion?	Advanced	
28	Infer the meaning of a phrase?	Advanced	
29	Recognise a feature of a text?	Advanced	
30	Infer a reason?	Advanced	
31	Establish a quality from a description?	Intermediate	
32	Infer the intended meaning from an expression?	Advanced	
33	Infer a reason for a situation?	Intermediate	
34	Sequence a series of events?	Intermediate	
35	Infer a reason for an action?	Advanced	

READING TEST 4

This is the final Reading Test. There are 35 questions.

If you aren't sure what to do, ask your teacher or your parents to help you. Don't be afraid to ask if it isn't clear to you.

Allow around 50 minutes for this test. Take a short break if necessary.

In this test you will need to look at a picture or read something first. Then read each question and colour in the circle with the correct answer. Sometimes you will have to write an answer in a space provided.

Read *The saltwater crocodile* and answer questions 1 to 7.

The saltwater crocodile

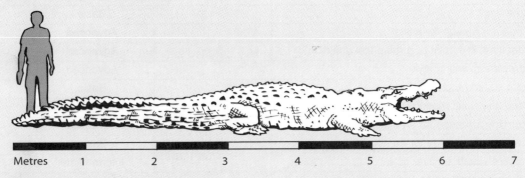

Metres 1 2 3 4 5 6 7

There are two types of crocodiles in Australia: the freshwater crocodile and the saltwater crocodile. Both are found in the tropical north. The 'freshie' is not a man-
5 eater and is much smaller than the saltwater crocodile, which will attack people.

The saltwater crocodile has a long, low lizard-shaped body. It has short legs, a powerful tail and long snout. Its teeth are
10 sharp, and it's the jaw that's most destructive. It can easily crush a large kangaroo. It is Australia's largest animal.

Saltwater crocodiles generally spend the tropical wet season in freshwater swamps
15 and rivers, moving downstream in the dry season as rivers and lagoons dry up. They often travel many kilometres out to sea.

The saltwater crocodile is a predator capable of taking most animals that enter its territory,
20 either on land or in the water.

It usually waits patiently for its prey to get close to the water's edge before striking suddenly, using its strength to drag the victim into the water. Animals are crushed by the
25 crocodile's jaw pressure, or drowned. It can drag a fully-grown buffalo into the water.

Its hunting style is called the 'death roll'. It grabs onto the animal and rolls powerfully. This throws any struggling animal off
30 balance, making it easier to drag it into the water. The 'death roll' is also used for tearing apart large animals once they are dead.

Crocodiles can reach speeds of 17 kph over short distances before they tire. They
35 can accelerate much faster over very short distances by exploding into action, covering 12 metres in less than a second—long enough to capture prey before it can react. It's no wonder rivers, beaches and waterholes in
40 northern Australia have *No Swimming* signs.

1. The saltwater crocodile and freshwater crocodile are
   - ○ about the same size.
   - ○ not the only types of Australian crocodile.
   - ○ as dangerous as each other.
   - ○ both found in northern Australia.

2. The importance of the picture is to
   - ○ show where to stand when near a crocodile.
   - ○ make obvious the size of a crocodile compared to a person.
   - ○ provide a warning about the dangers of the crocodile's tail.
   - ○ compare the difference in size of the legs and tail.

3. The most amazing feature of the saltwater crocodile is the
   - ○ kind of food it eats.
   - ○ speed at which it can catch its prey.
   - ○ long, low lizard-shaped body.
   - ○ distance it can travel out to sea.

4. The saltwater crocodile kills most of its prey with its
   - ○ teeth.
   - ○ claws.
   - ○ tail.
   - ○ jaws.

5. Which word best describes how a saltwater crocodile captures its prey?
   - ○ lurks
   - ○ traps
   - ○ tricks
   - ○ entices

6. The 'death roll' usually happens
   - ○ under the water's surface.
   - ○ when animals enter the water.
   - ○ at the water's edge.
   - ○ after a long chase.

7. According to the text, which statement about saltwater crocodiles is correct?
   - ○ They are fast in water but slow on land.
   - ○ They are not as dangerous as freshwater crocodiles.
   - ○ They are not found in fresh water.
   - ○ They are larger than any other Australian animal.

☞ Answers and explanations on pages 170–171

Read *How to make a paper hat* and answer questions 8 to 12.

How to make a paper hat

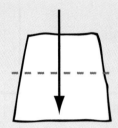

PAPER HATS ARE EASY TO MAKE — AND CHEAP!

1 Start with a full sheet of newspaper.

2 Fold on centre crease. Position the folded crease at the top of your workspace.

3 Fold top corner to centre line creating a diagonal crease.

4 Fold the other top corner to the centre line, creating a diagonal crease.

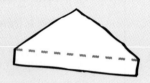

5 Fold up bottom edge top layer only, to cover the edge of the two previous folds.

6 Turn paper over. (Stop here for a pirate hat.)

7 Fold in the left outside edge partway to the centre of the paper.

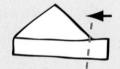

8 Fold in the right outside edge partway to the centre of the paper.

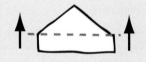

9 Adjust to fit. The distance between the outside edges can be adjusted, more or less, to fit the size of your head. Fold up the bottom edge.

10 Open your hat, and place on your head. Bingo!

Source: http://www.wikihow.com/Make-a-Paper-Hat

---

8. What is needed to make a paper hat?

○ scissors

○ sticky tape

○ ruler

○ newspaper

9. What is the main skill required to make a paper hat?

○ measuring

○ folding

○ cutting

○ drawing

10. If I only wanted to make a pirate's hat how many steps would I follow?

Write your answer on the line.

_____

11. The word *Bingo!* is used

○ as a cry of success.

○ to show that Step 10 is the last step.

○ as a call for help.

○ to show you are ready to start again.

12. This hat would be most suitable for

○ an important birthday party.

○ a windy weather day.

○ a pony rider.

○ a game with pretend characters.

Read *Leaving home* and answer questions 13 to 19.

Leaving home

Mum and Dad were very big when I was a baby. Even my cot was very big!

When I could crawl, it was a long way across the kitchen. It was even further to
5 the bathroom.

After I started to walk it was *still* a long way across the yard. The garage path was straight and hard.

On the times Dad and Mum took me to
10 the shops, the world spread out of sight. The streets were long and full of people. Around every corner was a new adventure. The streets seemed to go on forever.

I was scared the day I started school. It
15 was a long way from home. My desk was big. My classroom was large. The school was gigantic. There were many children I didn't know. Ms Green was my best friend.

For school excursions we went on long
20 trips to the park, the swimming pool and sometimes to the zoo. From the zoo I could see right to the end of the ocean. If I looked the other way, across the city I could see mountains. I wondered what
25 was over the other side. Did the world go on forever?

In Grade Two I am really big. I am as big as my friends. Jamie is my best friend. Sometimes I walk to school with Jamie.
30 He lives right up the end of our street. I am even allowed to ride my bike in the park. I am *quite* big.

I'll go to high school when I'm really big. I can hardly think that far. When I grow up
35 I might do exciting things. That's not for a long time!

Some nights I go and look at the stars in the black sky. Astronauts are in space. They fly around the Earth in spaceships.
40 For them the Earth looks really small.

When I grow up I want to be an astronaut. In space I will able to see the whole of Earth. It is just a tiny speck in a universe that goes on forever. I would like to go to a
45 star when I am big.

☞ Answers and explanations on page 171

13. It was a very long way for the narrator to crawl

○ to the bathroom.

○ across the yard.

○ to the shops.

○ down the street.

14. What made the narrator feel frightened?

○ riding a bike

○ the first day at school

○ getting lost in the shops

○ being in a spaceship

15. Which word best describes the narrator?

○ curious

○ fearful

○ daring

○ fussy

16. The text could best be called

○ a recount.

○ an explanation.

○ a narrative.

○ a description.

17. The text is mainly about

○ the first years at school.

○ how important teachers are as friends.

○ the importance of being brave.

○ how we see the world as we get older.

18. The narrator had a number of experiences. Write the numbers 1 to 4 in the boxes to show the order in which the narrator had the experiences.

1	crawling to the bathroom
3	walking to school
2	going to the shops
4	looking at the night-time sky

19. Another suitable title for the text would be

○ School excursions.

○ Riding to the park.

○ It's a big world.

○ Astronaut training.

Read *The witch* and answer questions 20 to 24.

The witch

There's a witch who lives in the tree outside,
Near the window next to my bed,
And she calls her friends from far and wide
To come to the feast she's spread.

5 She calls them to come with a 'Who?
   Who? Who?'
And her voice goes out on the breeze.
Then I hear them answer her, 'You!
   You! You!'
10 As their brooms rustle leaves in the trees.

Then she scratches her fingernails on the
   pane
Of the window next to my bed,
While I clutch the doona with all my might
15 And pull it over my head.

In the light of day I know she's been
For she's left a feather or two,
Pulled from the owl in the tree next door
And used to stir her brew.

20 One night I peeped through the window pane
As brave as I could be,
But all I could see was a lonely owl
On a branch in next door's tree.

Elaine Horsfield

20. This poem is about a child who

○ has a vivid imagination.

○ is afraid of owls.

○ cannot go to sleep.

○ has seen a witch.

21. The child believes the witch wants other witches *to come to the feast she's spread.* A feast that has been *spread* is one that is

○ already prepared.

○ not well organised.

○ over a large area.

○ messy-looking.

22. What is the most likely reason for the scratching sound on the windowpane?

○ the witches' brooms brushing as they pass by

○ fingernails across the glass

○ an owl scratching to get into the bedroom

○ a tree branch scraping across the glass

23. The child in bed pulls the doona over her head. This is because she

○ is getting cold.

○ is feeling scared.

○ doesn't like the night-time noises.

○ cannot get to sleep.

24. The word *Who* is repeated (*Who? Who? Who?*). This is because

○ the child is nervous and is not listening carefully.

○ the witch wants to make sure her friends hear her invitation.

○ it sounds like the call of a lonely owl.

○ the breeze is making the sound echo.

Read the *Beltana Station brochure* and answer questions 25 to 30.

This is the inside of a folded brochure for Beltana Station.

Beltana Station—Stay on a property with a difference

Beltana Station covers over 2000 square hectares and is a fully working sheep and cattle station, and a great place for a holiday with a *real* difference. Here the animals are not just to be looked at. They are part of everyday working life at the historic Beltana Station.

What to do

See how a station really works. Join in the daily working life with station staff.

Shearing, mustering and camp-outs are part of the Beltana Station's activities.

Farm animals to see: sheep, cattle, camels and alpacas.

For the kids, depending on the season, there will be animals to feed—chooks, lambs, calves and alpacas.

Alpacas graze against a backdrop of the Flinders Range.

The station is an outback inspiration for painters and photographers.

There is a family games room.

Three 4WD tracks through the station take in such sights as Lake Torrens, Mount Deception, relics in Old Beltana town and much more—self-drive or tag-along trips can be organised.

Accommodation includes:

- The historic 1860s shearers' quarters
- Two-room bush huts (1860s) in remote places
- Camping and caravan sites
- One historic country cottage

Visitors enjoy a break in the shearing shed.

Beltana Station is not a resort hotel.

Come to Beltana and experience real life with real people.

Adapted from Beltana information leaflet

25. For the visitor, Beltana Station is very much like a
   ○ large wild park.
   ○ real-life work experience.
   ○ relaxing, carefree vacation.
   ○ place for weekend picnics.

26. What would be a suitable activity for children at Beltana Station?
   ○ camp-outs with stockmen
   ○ round-up and pen cattle
   ○ sheep shearing
   ○ feeding lambs

☞ Answers and explanations on page 172

27. The station is an *inspiration for painters and photographers*. This means the station
- ○ has many exciting things to do.
- ○ stirs up strong emotions.
- ○ encourages people to do artistic things.
- ○ gives people ideas to try out.

28. A *tag-along trip* would be one where
- ○ drivers play chasing games in vehicles.
- ○ a trip with no real purpose.
- ○ one driver follows a leader in another car.
- ○ a vehicle is towed by another vehicle.

29. A visit to Beltana Station would be fascinating to a person wanting to
- ○ learn some Australian history.
- ○ go mountain hiking.
- ○ enjoy team sports.
- ○ have relaxing, leisure-time activities.

30. Why is a stay at Beltana Station called a *holiday with a real difference*?
Write your answer on the line.

_____

Read *Phillip Island—a restoration project* and answer questions 31 to 35.

Phillip Island—a restoration project

Phillip Island is an uninhabited island about 7 kilometres off the coast of Norfolk Island. It is interesting because the residents of Norfolk Island are working hard to restore
5 the island's natural beauty.

At one stage Norfolk Island was a penal settlement with soldiers as guards. The worst convicts from NSW were sent there to serve their prison sentences under
10 extremely harsh conditions. They were treated worse than slaves.

Reports from the early days of settlement describe Phillip Island as covered in lush green vegetation. It now has a reddish look
15 because of the exposed, eroded volcanic soil.

The change occurred because soldiers from the penal colony used the island for hunting, as well as a supply of fresh meat. It was a chance for the soldiers to
20 get a break from working as guards in the dreadful prisons. The soldiers brought rabbits, pigs and goats to the island. These animals soon multiplied. There were no natural enemies.

25 Soon the dense rainforests were almost wiped out by the animals. The rabbits ate the small plants for over 200 years. There was nothing to hold the soil in place. The rich topsoil was blown away, or washed into the sea during
30 heavy rain. The island was neglected until 1983 when it was decided to restore it to its original condition. The last rabbit was killed in the late 1980s. This allowed the remaining natural vegetation to survive.

35 Since then a slow reclamation has taken place. Work can only be done when the seas are not rough as the island can only be reached by sea. Once on the island, volunteers have a steep climb up to the
40 worksites. The work is not finished but real progress is being made.

☞ **Answers and explanations on page 173**

31. Who was responsible for introducing domestic animals to Phillip Island?

   ○ the soldiers who guarded the Norfolk Island prisoners

   ○ convicts from the prisons on Norfolk Island

   ○ volunteers who work on the island

   ○ the residents of Norfolk Island

32. The people who now visit Phillip Island could best be described as

   ○ dedicated.

   ○ fussy.

   ○ regretful.

   ○ casual.

33. Choose the statement about Phillip Island that is an opinion.

   ○ The introduced animals on Phillip Island had no natural enemy.

   ○ Phillip Island's topsoil was fertile and productive.

   ○ Phillip Island was not a suitable place for convicts.

   ○ The last rabbits on Phillip Island were killed in the 1980s.

34. Which word best describes how volunteers feel about the future of Phillip Island?

   ○ anxious

   ○ unexcited

   ○ gloomy

   ○ hopeful

35. Participants in the Phillip Island project would find it

   ○ arduous and rewarding.

   ○ dangerous and disappointing.

   ○ popular and exciting.

   ○ enjoyable and undemanding.

END OF TEST

Well done! You have completed the final Reading Test. It means that you have answered or attempted over 140 Reading questions. Now take a long break before you do any more tests.

How did you find the questions in this test? Were some hard for you? Check to see where you did well and where you had problems.

Use the diagnostic chart on page 95 to see which level of ability you reached. This is only an estimate. Don't be surprised if you answered some difficult questions correctly or even missed some easier questions.

Please note that multiple interpretations are possible for the levels of ability of these tasks. Also, some questions involve skills from different levels. This is only an initial guide to the approximate level of the reading skill assessed. No claim is made that this will be identical to the scores a student will receive in the actual tests, as the assessors will use a complex scoring system to estimate a student's level of ability.

☞ Answers and explanations on page 173

Instructions

- As you check the answer for each question, mark it as correct (✓) or incorrect (✗). Mark any questions that you omitted or left out as incorrect (✗) for the moment.
- Then look at how many you answered correctly in each level.
- You will be able to see what level you are at by finding the point where you started having consistent difficulty with questions. For example, if you answered most questions correctly up to the Intermediate level and then got most questions wrong from then onwards, it is likely your ability is at an Intermediate level. You can ask your parents or teacher to help you do this if this is not clear to you.

Am I able to ...

	SKILL	ESTIMATED LEVEL	✓ or ✗
1	Find a directly stated fact?	Basic	
2	Interpret the importance of a picture?	Intermediate	
3	Evaluate the relative importance of facts?	Intermediate	
4	Find information?	Intermediate	
5	Relate a word to an action?	Advanced	
6	Find information?	Intermediate	
7	Distinguish between facts and non-facts?	Basic	
8	Find a stated fact?	Basic	
9	Recognise the similarity of a sequence of actions?	Basic	
10	Select a specific piece of information?	Basic	
11	Interpret the meaning of idiom in context?	Intermediate	
12	Make a value judgement?	Intermediate	
13	Select a relevant fact?	Basic	
14	Find information?	Basic	
15	Relate a word to a behaviour?	Advanced	
16	Recognise a text type?	Advanced	
17	Make a generalisation?	Intermediate	
18	Sequence a series of events?	Intermediate	
19	Make a generalisation to select a suitable title?	Advanced	
20	Infer a characteristic?	Intermediate	
21	Interpret the meaning of idiom in context?	Advanced	
22	Interpret a reason for an action?	Intermediate	
23	Interpret a reason for an action?	Advanced	
24	Interpret the intent of a homonym as a literary device?	Intermediate	
25	Make a generalisation about a feature?	Intermediate	
26	Infer a suitable activity given a specific situation?	Intermediate	
27	Interpret a commonly used term?	Advanced	
28	Interpret idiom in context?	Advanced	
29	Infer a reason?	Intermediate	
30	Interpret advertising jargon?	Advanced	
31	Find a fact in a text?	Basic	
32	Relate a word to an attitude?	Advanced	
33	Distinguish between fact and opinion?	Advanced	
34	Relate a word to a feeling?	Advanced	
35	Predict a consequence from an action?	Advanced	

LANGUAGE CONVENTIONS TEST 1

This is the first Language Conventions Test. There are 50 questions.

If you aren't sure what to do, ask your teacher or your parents to help you. Don't be afraid to ask if it isn't clear to you.

Allow around 40 minutes for this test. Take a short break if necessary.

The spelling mistakes in these sentences have been circled.
Colour in the circle with the correct spelling.

1. Sandy has (replyed) to my party invitation.

   replied ○   replyd ○   repleid ○   repleyd ○

2. The falcon kept (swoopping) on the rabbits as they nibbled the grass.

   swoping ○   swooping ○   swopping ○   swoopin ○

3. The bus was (delaid) for at least ten minutes.

   delayed ○   delayied ○   delade ○   deleyed ○

4. The (referree) was disgusted by the shouts from the spectators.

   referee ○   refferree ○   refferee ○   refere ○

5. My aunt's new house is in a (centeral) location.

   centrall ○   centrale ○   central ○   sentral ○

6. How many (quarteres) make a whole?

   quartres ○   qarters ○   quarters ○   qaurters ○

7. The (spian) is another name for the backbone.

   spine ○   spaine ○   span ○   spiene ○

8. Bradley has a huge credit card (det). He owes hundreds of dollars.

   dete ○   debt ○   detb ○   diet ○

9. Not all (proffesors) are mad, you know!

   professors ○   professers ○   proffesers ○   proffessers ○

10. The choir sang (merryly) as the class filed into school.

    merryily ○   merrily ○   merily ○   merreyly ○

11. How many light (switchs) are there in the bedroom?

    switchers ○   swiches ○   swichers ○   switches ○

☞ Answers and explanations on page 174

LANGUAGE CONVENTIONS TEST 1

Look at the labelled drawing of the telephone. The spelling mistakes on the labels have been circled. Write the correct spelling of each word in the boxes.

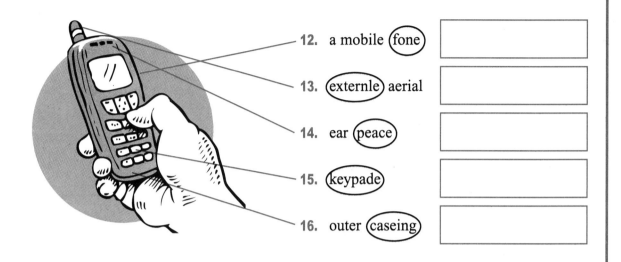

12. a mobile (fone)

13. (externle) aerial

14. ear (peace)

15. (keypade)

16. outer (caseing)

Read *Who were the gumdiggers?* Each pair of lines has one word that is incorrect. Write the correct spelling of each word in the boxes.

Who were the gumdiggers?

17. In New Zealand their is a tree whose sap, called gum, seeps from cracks in

18. the bark, then sets hard. Much of it falls to the grownd and is collected, but

19. because the trees wunce grew near swamps some of it fell into mud and

20. sank. Later, the men who came allong to dig it up were called gumdiggers.

☞ **Answers and explanations on page 174**

LANGUAGE CONVENTIONS TEST 1

Read the sentences. Each sentence has one word that is incorrect.
Write the correct spelling of each word in the boxes.

21. Some birds have femail chicks that are larger than the male chicks.

22. Mitch tried to ballance a ball on the top of an orange traffic cone.

23. "You should be thankfull that you have a meal!" said Dad seriously.

24. The chemist gave sensible advise without charging.

25. My favourite green vegetable is cellary.

Colour in the circle with the correct answer.

26. Which word correctly completes this sentence?

The plane [____] across the sky before disappearing behind a cloud.

fly	flew	flied	flewed
○	○	○	○

27. Which word correctly completes this sentence?

The price of jeans [____] too high.

are	were	is	am
○	○	○	○

28. Which word correctly completes this sentence?

Two [____] were trapped in floodwaters on a back road near Marree.

4Wd's	4WD's	4WDs	4wds
○	○	○	○

29. Which word in this sentence is a conjunction (joining word)?

The boys played well but the girls were magnificent on the day.

The	but	magnificent	on
○	○	○	○

☞ **Answers and explanations on page 174**

30. Which word correctly completes this sentence?

It was six ▨▨▨▨ before the repairman rang to say he'd be late!

o'clock	o clock	o-clock	oclock
○	○	○	○

31. Which word or words correctly complete this sentence?

The cups were ▨▨▨▨ top of the bench.

upon	at the	on	up
○	○	○	○

32. Which sentence has the correct punctuation?

○ Why she did it, I'll never know?

○ Why do you put sugar in your tea?

○ Why the sky is blue?

○ Why I can do the task is because I practise a lot?

33. Which word correctly completes this sentence?

▨▨▨▨ you ride your bike to school or walk I don't really care.

Whether	Because	Although	Regardless
○	○	○	○

34. Which word correctly completes this sentence?

The oil spill was a disaster! The whole ▨▨▨▨ feathers were black with oil.

flocks	flocks'	flock's	flocks's
○	○	○	○

35. Which words correctly complete this sentence?

We waited until ten-thirty ▨▨▨▨ .

○ or there was no sign of the cleaners

○ but there was no call from our visitors

○ because it was late in the morning

○ the news came on

☞ Answers and explanations on pages 174–175

36. Which words and punctuation correctly complete this sentence?

"I went to see an action _____ film did you see?" asked Bryan.

○ movie what

○ movie? What

○ movie. What

○ movie, "What

37. Which word correctly completes this sentence?

We played billiards which _____ a difficult game for short people.

are	were	am	is
○	○	○	○

38. Which words or letters correctly complete this sentence?

The sailors on the ship _____ *Walrus* are due to arrive in port on Friday.

HMAS	H.M.A.S.	Hmas	HMAS.
○	○	○	○

39. Which sentence has the correct punctuation?

○ Anya said, "What do we do with the leftover food?"

○ Anya said, "What do we do with the leftover food"?

○ Anya said ",What do we do with the leftover food?"

○ Anya said "What do we do with the leftover food?"

40. Which word should **not** have a capital letter?

My Brother, Jack, and I read Batman comics in our bedroom.

⭡ ⭡ ⭡ ⭡
○ ○ ○ ○

41. Which words can all be adverbs?

○ lonely, hers, silly, fairy

○ cleverly, almost, soon, wildly

○ happy, lost, several, frightened

○ around, in, beside, with

42. Which word correctly completes this sentence?

We went to see a *Harry Potter* film ▮▮▮▮▮ was on at the Regent Theatre.

what   who   which   that

○   ○   ○   ○

43. An apostrophe has been left out of this sentence.
Where should the missing apostrophe go?

○   ○   ○   ○
↓   ↓   ↓   ↓

Mae thought the pen s were her s but we all know they we re from Pam s collection.

Read *Elephant's complaint*. The text has some gaps. Choose the correct word or words to fill each gap.

Elephant's complaint

44. Way down south where ▮▮▮▮▮ grow,

banana	bananas	the banana	a bananas
○	○	○	○

45. A grasshopper stepped on an elephant's ▮▮▮▮ .

tow	foot	toe	show
○	○	○	○

46. The elephant said, with tears in his ▮▮▮▮

eyes,	eyes	eyes.	eyes!
○	○	○	○

47. "Pick on somebody ▮▮▮▮ own size!"

you're	your	youre	you'r
○	○	○	○

Colour in the circle with the correct answer.

48. Which sentence has the correct punctuation?

○ Workers at the General Post Office (GPO) are striking for higher wages. Officials at the GPO were not prepared for the strike.

○ Workers at the General Post Office (GPO) are striking for higher wages. Officials at the (GPO) were not prepared for the strike.

○ Workers at the (General Post Office) GPO are striking for higher wages. Officials at the GPO were not prepared for the strike.

○ Workers (at the General Post Office) GPO are striking for higher wages. Officials (at the GPO) were not prepared for the strike.

49. Which words correctly complete this sentence?

The dogs were running across the beach ▮▮▮▮▮ .

○ which had no collars

○ that annoyed swimmers.

○ that belonged to the tourists

○ looking for food scraps

50. Which is the correct order for the three missing words?

Have you seen our ▮▮▮▮▮ cattle dog?

○ old, big, Australian

○ Australian, old, big

○ big, old, Australian

○ old, Australian, big

END OF TEST

Well done! You have completed the first Language Conventions Test.

How did you go with these test questions? Some were harder than the sample questions. Turn to the next page and mark your work. Check to see where you did well and where you had problems. Make sure you focus on the questions you answered incorrectly or found difficult. Try to understand the explanations given to you and learn from them so you can apply them to other questions—this is how you can improve.

There are now three more tests, each containing 50 questions. They include many of the same types of questions, plus a few new types.

☞ **Answers and explanations on page 175**

CHECK YOUR SKILLS: LANGUAGE CONVENTIONS TEST 1

Instructions

- As you check the answer for each question, mark it as correct (✓) or incorrect (✗). Mark any questions that you omitted or left out as incorrect (✗) for the moment.
- Then look at how many you answered correctly in each level.
- You will be able to see what level you are at by finding the point where you started having consistent difficulty with questions. For example, if you answered most questions correctly up to the Intermediate level and then got most questions wrong from then onwards, it is likely your ability is at an Intermediate level. You can ask your parents or teacher to help you do this if it isn't clear to you.

Am I able to ...

	SKILL	ESTIMATED LEVEL	✓ or ✗
1	Spell words ending with a consonant and *y* and add an *ed* suffix?	Basic	
2	Spell a common word that ends in *ing*?	Basic	
3	Spell words ending with vowel and *y* and add an *ed* suffix?	Intermediate	
4	Spell less usual words containing confusing double letters?	Advanced	
5	Spell a common word?	Intermediate	
6	Spell a common school mathematics word?	Intermediate	
7	Spell a simple single-syllable word?	Basic	
8	Spell a difficult word with a silent *b*?	Advanced	
9	Spell less usual words containing confusing double letters?	Intermediate	
10	Spell words ending with a consonant and *y* and add an *ly* suffix?	Intermediate	
11	Recognise the correct spelling of a plural of a word that ends in *ch*?	Intermediate	
12	Spell a common word with a *ph* letter sound?	Basic	
13	Spell a multisyllabic word?	Intermediate	
14	Spell a common homonym?	Intermediate	
15	Spell a common compound word?	Basic	
16	Spell words ending with a consonant and *e* and add an *ing* suffix?	Intermediate	
17	Spell a common homonym?	Basic	
18	Spell a common word?	Intermediate	
19	Spell a difficult single-syllable word?	Advanced	
20	Spell a commonly misspelled word?	Intermediate	
21	Spell a commonly misspelled word?	Intermediate	
22	Spell frequently used words with unfamiliar spelling patterns?	Advanced	
23	Spell a common word with a *ful* suffix?	Intermediate	
24	Spell a commonly misused, misspelled word?	Advanced	
25	Spell a less usual word?	Advanced	
26	Recognise the correct use of an irregular verb?	Basic	
27	Identify correct use of an abstract noun–verb agreement?	Advanced	
28	Recognise the plural form of words reduced to numbers and initials?	Advanced	
29	Recognise a conjunction in context?	Basic	

CHECK YOUR SKILLS: LANGUAGE CONVENTIONS TEST 1

	SKILL	ESTIMATED LEVEL	✓ or ✗
30	Recognise the correct form of a shortened word?	Intermediate	
31	Recognise the correct preposition in context?	Intermediate	
32	Recognise the correct form of a question?	Intermediate	
33	Recognise the correct conjunction to begin a sentence?	Intermediate	
34	Use an apostrophe of possession correctly with a collective noun?	Intermediate	
35	Complete a sentence with a coordinate clause joined with a suitable conjunction?	Advanced	
36	Use the correct stop in a multi-sentence passage?	Intermediate	
37	Identify correct use of a singular noun–verb agreement?	Intermediate	
38	Recognise the correct form of titles reduced to initials?	Intermediate	
39	Recognise the correct punctuation for direct speech?	Advanced	
40	Recognise when to use a capital letter?	Basic	
41	Recognise words that can be adverbs?	Intermediate	
42	Recognise the correct pronoun for an object?	Intermediate	
43	Recognise the correct use of an apostrophe of possession?	Intermediate	
44	Use the correct (definite) article for a plural noun?	Basic	
45	Recognise the correct spelling of a rhyming word in context?	Intermediate	
46	Use the correct punctuation at the end of a line of poetry?	Intermediate	
47	Distinguish between an adjective and a shortened word?	Intermediate	
48	Recognise the correct use of brackets for a term referred to by initials?	Advanced	
49	Correctly use a subordinate clause (adjectival)?	Advanced	
50	Correctly sequence a series of adjectives?	Advanced	

LANGUAGE CONVENTIONS TEST 2

This is the second Language Conventions Test. There are 50 questions.

If you aren't sure what to do, ask your teacher or your parents to help you. Don't be afraid to ask if it isn't clear to you.

Allow around 40 minutes for this test. Take a short break if necessary.

The spelling mistakes in these sentences have been circled.
Colour in the circle with the correct spelling.

1. The (sheerer) got hot and sweaty while working in the shed.

shaerer	shearer	sherer	sherrer
○	○	○	○

2. Plants may live for a long time but no plant lives (fourever).

foreever	fourevor	forevver	forever
○	○	○	○

3. The (flourist) had a huge supply of roses for Mother's Day.

florist	florest	flourest	flowerist
○	○	○	○

4. The (mattron) quietly checked the patients as they slept.

matren	matrun	matron	matrone
○	○	○	○

5. The council in each city has a lord (mair).

mayor	mare	major	mayer
○	○	○	○

6. The hail damaged many ripening (cherrys).

cheries	cherries	cherryes	cheeryies
○	○	○	○

7. Trixie had (tidyed) her room before breakfast!

tidyied	tidied	tirdied	tided
○	○	○	○

8. Are both lemons and oranges (sitrus) fruit?

sitres	citrus	cittrus	citrust
○	○	○	○

9. The hose to the dishwasher had frayed and Dad called in a (plummer).

plumer	plummar	plumber	plumbber
○	○	○	○

10. Sugar possums were (glideing) from the tops of mountain gum trees.

glideng	gliding	glieding	gliden
○	○	○	○

11. Our class had a new (theam) to work on. It was called *The Great Explorers*.

theame	theem	theeme	theme
○	○	○	○

☞ **Answers and explanations on pages 175–176**

LANGUAGE CONVENTIONS TEST 2

Look at the labelled drawing. The spelling mistakes on the labels have been circled.
Write the correct spelling for each word in the boxes.

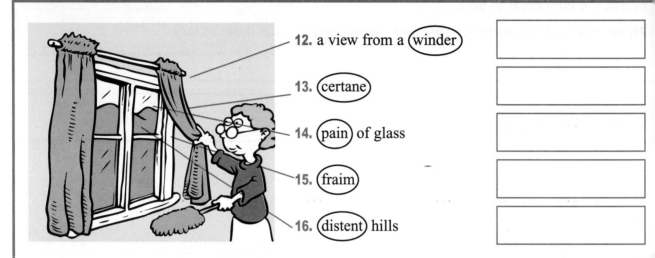

12. a view from a (winder)

13. (certane)

14. (pain) of glass

15. (fraim)

16. (distent) hills

Read *Cape York Peninsula.* Each sentence has one word that is incorrect.
Write the correct spelling of each word in the boxes.

Cape York Peninsula

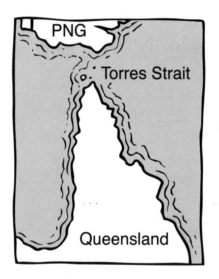

17. Cape York Peninsula is the pointy seckion
of Queensland's north. It is a large

18. area of land, offen called The Tip, because
it is the most northerly point of the

19. Australian continent. The meny islands
of Torres Strait are even further north.

20. Torres Strait is the sea gap bertween
The Tip and Papua New Guinea (PNG).

☞ **Answers and explanations on page 176**

LANGUAGE CONVENTIONS TEST 2

Read the sentences. Each sentence has one word that is incorrect. Write the correct spelling of each word in the boxes.

21. The water for our table was slow to bring our meals.

22. "That's very noughty," said my grandmother crossly.

23. There were seats for parents and hichares for babies at the nursery.

24. The scout leader planned a mystry excursion into the pine forest.

25. The officer was typeing up a report when we entered her office.

Colour in the circle with the correct answer.

26. Which word correctly completes this sentence?

I don't know how it happened but ⬛⬛⬛⬛ lost the only key!

your	your've	you're	you've
○	○	○	○

27. Which word correctly completes this sentence?

Bill and Joe ⬛⬛⬛⬛ to the coaching college every Thursday.

goes	go	going	gone
○	○	○	○

28. Which word correctly completes this sentence?

Josh has ⬛⬛⬛⬛ a new pair of running shoes for the marathon.

bought	buyed	buying	buy
○	○	○	○

29. Which sentence has the correct punctuation?
   ○ Ms Ghan said to me, "Time to stop writing."
   ○ Ms Ghan said, "To me, time to stop writing."
   ○ Ms Ghan said to me. "Time to stop writing."
   ○ Ms Ghan said to me, Time to stop writing.

☞ **Answers and explanations on page 176**

LANGUAGE CONVENTIONS TEST 2

Read *Flag colours*. The text has some gaps.
Choose the correct word(s) and punctuation to fill each gap.

Flag colours

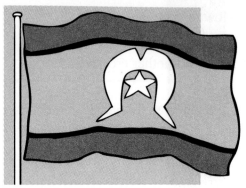

30. The colours on flags are not there for decoration. The flag of the Torres Strait ▦ has four colours.

    ○ islanders
    ○ Islanders
    ○ islanders,
    ○ Islanders,

31. The colours of green, blue, ▦ stand for land, sea, peace and the Indigenous people.

    ○ white and black
    ○ white and, black
    ○ white, and black
    ○ white and black.

32. In the central blue band is a white headdress above ▦ five-pointed star.

an	the	a	that
○	○	○	○

33. The ▦ design was the result of a competition held in June 1992. It is now an official Australian flag.

flags'	flag's	Flag's	flags
○	○	○	○

Colour in the circle(s) with the correct answer.

---

34. Which sentence has the correct punctuation?

    ○ Oh, is that the time?
    ○ While I'm there, I'll get the bread?
    ○ It must be six o'clock because the lights have come on?
    ○ Why he doesn't own up I'll never know?

☞ **Answers and explanations on page 176**

35. Which word correctly completes this sentence?

We could see ▨▨▨▨▨ Kosciuszko from the Alpine Way.

mt	Mt	Mt.	mt.
○	○	○	○

36. Which words should be used instead of *ain't* in this sentence?

He ain't going to give me a go on his bike!

are not	will not	is not	am not
○	○	○	○

37. An apostrophe has been left out of this sentence.

Where should the missing apostrophe go?

My aunt s glasses   were put beside her library books.

38. Which words can all be prepositions?
- ○ bridge, sky, wall, oval
- ○ whose, who, which, what
- ○ top, bottom, side, back
- ○ above, between, during, off

39. Which is the correct order for the three missing words?

The team consisted of ▨▨▨▨▨ players.
- ○ several, tall, basketball
- ○ tall, basketball, several
- ○ tall, several, basketball
- ○ several, basketball, tall

40. Which word correctly completes this sentence?

Olivia ▨▨▨▨▨ hard but she cannot touch her toes.

try	try's	tries	trie's
○	○	○	○

41. Which word correctly completes this sentence?

Right now the police [____] on the alert for a drunken driver.

is	were	was	are
○	○	○	○

42. Which words correctly complete this sentence?

Lenny washed the dishes [____] he [____] wiped them.

- ○ either—or
- ○ neither—nor
- ○ but—also
- ○ both—and

43. Which word correctly completes this sentence?

We don't know [____] coming so we should get more chairs, just in case.

who's	whose	who	who'se
○	○	○	○

44. Which word correctly completes this sentence?

Dad shared the balloons [____] all the children at the party.

among	between	in	with
○	○	○	○

45. Two commas (**,**) have been left out of this sentence.

Where should the missing commas go?

If you look over there you will see the red bull   the brown cows and the small calves.

46. Which sentence has the correct punctuation at the end?

- ○ How you did it, I will never know?
- ○ How you did it, I will never know.
- ○ How you did it, I will never know!
- ○ How you did it, I will never know,

☞ **Answers and explanations on page 177**

47. Which word in this sentence is a verb (doing word)?

The trickling creek bubbled across the rocks into a sparkling pool.

trickling	bubbled	across	sparkling
○	○	○	○

48. Which word or words correctly complete this sentence?

Marty said the ▮▮▮▮▮ thing I have ever heard!

silly	more sillier	silliest	most silliest
○	○	○	○

49. Which sentence has the correct punctuation?

○ The sugar glider (*petaurus brevicepos*) is a small possum that has the ability to glide from tree to tree.

○ The (sugar glider) *petaurus brevicepos* is a small possum that has the ability to glide from tree to tree.

○ The sugar glider (*petaurus brevicepos*) is (a small possum) that has the ability to glide from tree to tree.

○ The sugar glider *petaurus brevicepos* is a small possum that has the ability to glide (from tree to tree).

50. There are four boys in the house across the street. They play cards at night.

Which of the sentences below is closest in meaning to these sentences?

○ The four boys in the house across the street play cards all night.

○ Some of the boys in the house across the street play cards every night.

○ The boys in the house across the street play cards nightly.

○ All the boys in the house across the street play cards all night.

·······

END OF TEST

Well done! You have completed the second Language Conventions Test. We really mean this as there were many questions to answer.

How did you go with these test questions? Some were harder than the last test. Turn to the next page and mark your work. Check to see where you did well and where you had problems. Make sure you focus on the questions you answered incorrectly or found difficult. Try to understand the explanations given to you and learn from them so you can apply them to other questions—this is how you can improve.

There are now two more tests that each contain 50 questions. They include many of the same type of questions, plus a few new types.

☞ **Answers and explanations on page 177**

Instructions

- As you check the answer for each question, mark it as correct (✓) or incorrect (✗). Mark any questions that you omitted or left out as incorrect (✗) for the moment.

- Then look at how many you answered correctly in each level.

- You will be able to see what level you are at by finding the point where you started having consistent difficulty with questions. For example, if you answered most questions correctly up to the Intermediate level and then got most questions wrong from then onwards, it is likely your ability is at an Intermediate level. You can ask your parents or teacher to help you do this if it isn't clear to you.

Am I able to ...

	SKILL	ESTIMATED LEVEL	✓ or ✗
1	Spell a common occupational name?	Basic	
2	Spell a common compound word?	Basic	
3	Spell a less common occupational name?	Intermediate	
4	Spell a less common occupational compound word?	Intermediate	
5	Spell an occupational name with a less regular spelling pattern?	Advanced	
6	Spell the plural of a word ending with a consonant and *y*?	Intermediate	
7	Make the past tense of a word ending with a consonant and *y*?	Intermediate	
8	Spell a word with an unusual spelling?	Advanced	
9	Spell a word with a silent *b*?	Advanced	
10	Add the suffix *ing* to a word ending with a consonant and *e*?	Intermediate	
11	Spell an unusual sounding word?	Advanced	
12	Spell a common two-syllable word?	Intermediate	
13	Spell a common two-syllable word?	Intermediate	
14	Recognise and spell the correct homonym?	Advanced	
15	Spell a common single-syllable word?	Basic	
16	Spell a common two-syllable word?	Intermediate	
17	Spell a common word with a *tion* ending?	Intermediate	
18	Spell a commonly misspelled, mispronounced word with a silent letter?	Intermediate	
19	Spell a common word with a less regular pronunciation?	Basic	
20	Spell a common, two-syllable word	Intermediate	
21	Spell a common occupational name?	Intermediate	
22	Spell a difficult *aught* word?	Advanced	
23	Recognise the correct spelling of a plural, in context, of a word that contains a 'reasonable' alternative spelling?	Intermediate	
24	Spell a three-syllable word that is often poorly pronounced?	Advanced	
25	Add the suffix *ing* to a word ending with a consonant and *e*?	Advanced	
26	Select the correct contraction from a selection of similar sounding words?	Advanced	
27	Recognise common grammatical conventions (noun–verb agreement)?	Intermediate	
28	Recognise irregular verbs in context?	Basic	
29	Select a sentence using correct speech punctuation?	Intermediate	
30	Select the correct form of a (proper) noun?	Intermediate	

	SKILL	ESTIMATED LEVEL	✓ or ✗
31	Recognise the correct punctuation format for the last two words in a series joined by *and*?	Intermediate	
32	Recognise the correct article to be used with a word beginning with a consonant?	Basic	
33	Recognise the correct position for an apostrophe of possession?	Intermediate	
34	Recognise a question?	Basic	
35	Recognise the correct form of an abbreviation?	Intermediate	
36	Recognise the correct form of a commonly misused word?	Basic	
37	Locate an apostrophe of possession in context?	Intermediate	
38	Recognise words that can be prepositions?	Advanced	
39	Use adjectives in correct sequence?	Advanced	
40	Select the correct word from several similar sounding words in a noun/verb agreement context?	Intermediate	
41	Recognise common grammatical conventions (noun–verb agreement)?	Intermediate	
42	Correctly use paired conjunctions?	Intermediate	
43	Select the correct location for an apostrophe in an abbreviation?	Advanced	
44	Select the correct preposition for a common speech error?	Advanced	
45	Place commas correctly in a series of terms?	Advanced	
46	Recognise the correct stop in a two-part sentence?	Advanced	
47	Recognise a verb in context?	Intermediate	
48	Use comparative adjectives correctly?	Intermediate	
49	Recognise the correct use of brackets?	Advanced	
50	Interpret meaning in a short passage?	Advanced	

LANGUAGE CONVENTIONS TEST 3

This is the third Language Conventions Test. There are 50 questions.

If you aren't sure what to do, ask your teacher or your parents to help you. Don't be afraid to ask if it isn't clear to you.

Allow around 40 minutes for this test. Take a short break if necessary.

The spelling mistakes in these sentences have been circled.
Colour in the circle with the correct spelling.

1. Jason (colored) the sky bright green!

   colorred ○   coloured ○   colloured ○   colourd ○

2. I thought I saw (bullys) waiting near the gate, but I was wrong.

   bulleys ○   bullyes ○   bullies ○   bullyies ○

3. Birds of prey have sharp (clawes).

   claws ○   cloors ○   clorse ○   klaws ○

4. This sentence should end with an (exclaimation) mark.

   ○ exclamashion
   ○ exclamation
   ○ exclaimashun
   ○ exclammation

5. There was a (perple) stamp on the envelope.

   purpal ○   perpal ○   purrpal ○   purple ○

6. The wicketkeeper took three (catchs) in the last match.

   catchers ○   catches ○   caches ○   katches ○

7. The fox was onto the (sent) of a small rabbit.

   cent ○   sant ○   scant ○   scent ○

8. I want to be a (machanick) when I leave school.

   mechanick ○   mechanic ○   machanic ○   merchanic ○

9. The batteries are flat in my (digitall) camera.

   digital ○   digertal ○   dijital ○   diggital ○

☞ Answers and explanations on page 177

10. The (feild) was full of daisies.

fild	field	feeled	fieled
○	○	○	○

11. "Did you (imform) your teacher about your homework?"

inforn	infurm	inform	imforn
○	○	○	○

Look at the labelled drawing. The spelling mistakes on the labels have been circled. Write the correct spelling of each word in the boxes.

12. facial (featchers)

13. neatly (commed) hair

14. (forhead)

15. nose (brige)

16. left (cheak)

Read *Party preparations*. Each sentence has one word that is incorrect. Write the correct spelling of each word in the boxes.

Party preparations

17. "Who has to blow up the baloons?" called Dad from the kitchen.

18. "I expected Toby to do that. He's full of hot wind!" Mum shouted jokeingly.

19. "Hey! Why is everybody allways picking on me?" objected Toby.

20. "If you want yore party to be a success you need to hurry up," said Dad.

Read the sentences. Each sentence has one word that is incorrect.
Write the correct spelling of each word in the boxes.

21. Most people are very carefull when climbing over fences.

22. "That's vary stupid," said my uncle when I slid across the floor.

23. Our team debaited well but the visitors had better arguments.

24. Did the judge condem the prisoner to hard labour?

25. The bean seeds were berryed in straight rows by the garage wall.

Colour in the circle with the correct answer.

26. Which word correctly completes this sentence?

"What do ▮▮▮▮▮ want to do today for sport?" asked the teacher.

yous	you	Youse	youse
○	○	○	○

27. Which word in this sentence should have a capital letter?

"The council in this irish town has banned the use of poisons," explained the councillor.

28. Which sentence has the correct punctuation?
- ○ The teacher asked if any child felt sick?
- ○ The teacher asked if any child felt sick.
- ○ The teacher asked, "if any child felt sick."
- ○ The teacher asked if, "any child felt sick?"

LANGUAGE CONVENTIONS TEST 3

Read *The biggest lagoon*. The text has some gaps.
Choose the correct word(s) and punctuation to fill each gap.

The biggest lagoon

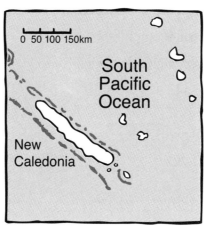

29. A lagoon is an area of water inside a coral reef which forms a partial barrier ▮▮▮ the open sea.

at	in	by	to
○	○	○	○

30. The island of New Caledonia boasts the largest lagoon in the world. It is surrounded by a 1600 ▮▮▮ coral reef.

km	km.	Km.	KM
○	○	○	○

31. This is the ▮▮▮ second largest coral reef and is home to 900 varieties of coral.

world's	worlds	World's	worlds'
○	○	○	○

32. The lagoon was recently added to the World Heritage List, a companion for Australia's ▮▮▮ .

- ○ great Barrier Reef
- ○ Great Barrier reef
- ○ great barrier reef
- ○ Great Barrier Reef

Colour in the circle with the correct answer.

33. Which word in this sentence is a preposition (a word indicating place)?

As the police struggled over the ridge, the bushrangers were taking a quiet rest.

ridge	over	quiet	rest
○	○	○	○

☞ Answers and explanations on page 178

34. Which sentence has the correct punctuation?

○ I let my dog, Flossy, have a run along the beach.

○ I let my dog Flossy, have a run along the beach.

○ I let my dog, Flossy have a run along the beach.

○ I let my dog Flossy have a run along the beach.

35. Which word correctly completes this sentence?

I checked my purse and ten dollars _____ all that I had.

are	were	was	what
○	○	○	○

36. Which word correctly completes this sentence?

The phone _____ but Mike didn't answer it. He was asleep!

rang	ringed	ranged	ring
○	○	○	○

37. Which word correctly completes this sentence?

There is a storm coming so _____ play the rest of the match tomorrow.

well	we'll	w'ell	wi'll
○	○	○	○

38. Which word correctly completes this sentence?

My parrot is a better talker _____ yours.

and	then	or	than
○	○	○	○

39. Which word or words correctly complete this sentence?

Sheryl was _____ than her sister at the presentation of awards.

more cheerful	cheerfuller	cheerifullest	most cheerful
○	○	○	○

40. Which words from this sentence should be in brackets ( )?

Driving through the Mitchell Plateau of Western Australia, we saw many Fan Palms *Livistonia eastonii* growing in areas of high rainfall.

○ Mitchell Plateau   ○ of Western Australia

○ Fan Palms   ○ *Livistonia eastonii*

LANGUAGE CONVENTIONS TEST 3

41. Which is the correct order for the three missing words?

There were ▨▨▨▨ apples on the kitchen table.

four, big, red	four, red, big	big, four, red	red, big, four
○	○	○	○

42. Which sentence uses the apostrophe correctly?

○ These are my shoes and your's are over there!

○ They've made a mistake in my exam paper!

○ Mr Jones' need to get a new car!

○ There were six glasses' in the box but three were cracked!

43. Which word in this sentence is an adverb?

They left the school early but missed the last bus home.

left	early	but	last
○	○	○	○

44. Which sentence has the correct punctuation?

○ Rotten fruit smelly bread and squashed cans littered the supermarket car park.

○ Rotten fruit, smelly bread and squashed cans littered the supermarket car park.

○ Rotten, fruit, smelly, bread and squashed cans littered the supermarket car park.

○ Rotten fruit, smelly bread, and squashed cans, littered the supermarket car park.

45. Which word correctly completes this sentence?

The book was leaning ▨▨▨▨ the computer on Rae's desk.

by	against	at	up
○	○	○	○

46. Which words can all be conjunctions (words that join together two other words or word groups)?

○ in, beside, underneath, smother

○ but, nor, while, although

○ union, connect, both, mix

○ the, those, them, itself

☞ **Answers and explanations on page 178**

47. Which word can be used instead of the underlined words?

Mum sent invitations to her sisters and brothers and her close cousins. She wanted <u>her sisters and brothers and her close cousins</u> to come to her party.

them	it	they	her
○	○	○	○

48. Which word and punctuation correctly completes this sentence?

"Tomorrow will be ▮▮▮▮▮ said Paula, "and we can go to the beach."

Friday,"	Friday"	Friday,	Friday."
○	○	○	○

49. Which letters or words from this sentence should be in brackets ( )?

The Roads and Traffic Authority RTA has an office in Parramatta, NSW.

○ Roads and Traffic Authority
○ RTA
○ Parramatta
○ NSW

50. Which words best complete this sentence?

A dog was found by a policewoman ▮▮▮▮▮ .

○ with long fluffy ears
○ chasing children noisily in the park
○ while on patrol by the river
○ wandering without a leash

END OF TEST

Well done! You have completed the third Language Conventions Test. We really mean this as there were many questions to answer.

How did you go with these test questions? Some were harder than the last test. Turn to the next page and mark your work. Check to see where you did well and where you had problems. Make sure you focus on the questions you answered incorrectly or found difficult. Try to understand the explanations given to you and learn from them so you can apply them to other questions—this is how you can improve.

There is now only one more test to complete. It contains 50 questions. It includes many of the same types of questions, plus a few new types.

Instructions

- As you check the answer for each question, mark it as correct (✓) or incorrect (✗). Mark any questions that you omitted or left out as incorrect (✗) for the moment.
- Then look at how many you answered correctly in each level.
- You will be able to see what level you are at by finding the point where you started having consistent difficulty with questions. For example, if you answered most questions correctly up to the Intermediate level and then got most questions wrong from then onwards, it is likely your ability is at an Intermediate level. You can ask your parents or teacher to help you do this if it isn't clear to you.

Am I able to ...

	SKILL	ESTIMATED LEVEL	✓ or ✗
1	Spell a frequently used school word?	Basic	
2	Make a plural from a word ending in a consonant and **y**?	Intermediate	
3	Spell the plural of a common word by adding **s**?	Basic	
4	Spell a frequently used school word?	Intermediate	
5	Spell a common word with a regular pattern?	Basic	
6	Spell the plural of a common word ending in **ch**?	Basic	
7	Recognise the correct homonym in context?	Intermediate	
8	Spell a common word with a less frequent letter pattern?	Advanced	
9	Spell a common word with a less regular letter/sound pattern?	Advanced	
10	Apply the **i** before **e** rule in a common situation?	Intermediate	
11	Spell a commonly used two-syllable word?	Intermediate	
12	Spell a common word with a less regular letter/sound pattern?	Advanced	
13	Spell a common word with a silent **b**?	Intermediate	
14	Spell a compound word?	Intermediate	
15	Spell a common word with a less regular letter/sound pattern?	Intermediate	
16	Spell a common word with a vowel blend?	Basic	
17	Spell a common word with a double letter pattern?	Intermediate	
18	Spell a basic word with two suffixes?	Advanced	
19	Spell a commonly misspelled two-syllable word?	Intermediate	
20	Recognise the correct spelling of a common homonym?	Basic	
21	Add the suffix **ful** to a common one-syllable word?	Intermediate	
22	Recognise the correct spelling of a common homonym?	Intermediate	
23	Spell a frequently used two-syllable school word?	Intermediate	
24	Spell a difficult word with a silent **n**?	Advanced	
25	Recognise the correct spelling of a common homonym and add a suffix?	Advanced	
26	Use the correct word instead of a commonly misused word?	Basic	
27	Select a word requiring a capital letter?	Basic	
28	Recognise the correct punctuation for indirect speech?	Intermediate	
29	Select the most appropriate preposition?	Intermediate	

	SKILL	ESTIMATED LEVEL	✓ or ✗
30	Select the correct abbreviation for a mathematical measurement?	Intermediate	
31	Recognise the location of an apostrophe for possession?	Intermediate	
32	Apply capital letters to a multi-word title?	Intermediate	
33	Recognise a preposition in context?	Advanced	
34	Recognise the correct location of commas in relation to a phrase in a sentence?	Advanced	
35	Recognise common grammatical conventions for money (noun–verb agreement)?	Intermediate	
36	Recognise an irregular verb in context?	Intermediate	
37	Recognise a common abbreviation?	Intermediate	
38	Recognise the correct usage of *than* as a conjunction?	Intermediate	
39	Select the correct term for a comparative adjective?	Intermediate	
40	Use brackets correctly for a scientific name?	Advanced	
41	Sequence adjectives correctly?	Intermediate	
42	Select an example of an apostrophe (for abbreviation) used correctly?	Intermediate	
43	Select an adverb in context?	Intermediate	
44	Punctuate with commas a series of terms?	Intermediate	
45	Select the correct preposition in context?	Intermediate	
46	Recognise words that can be conjunctions?	Intermediate	
47	Substitute a pronoun for a group of people?	Basic	
48	Place punctuation correctly in direct speech?	Advanced	
49	Correctly locate brackets around initials for a place name?	Advanced	
50	Correctly place a modifying phrase near its subject?	Advanced	

LANGUAGE CONVENTIONS TEST 4

This is the last Language Conventions Test. There are 50 questions.

If you aren't sure what to do, ask your teacher or your parents to help you. Don't be afraid to ask if it isn't clear to you.

Allow around 40 minutes for this test. Take a short break if necessary.

The spelling mistakes in these sentences have been circled.
Colour in the circle with the correct spelling.

1. Peter was (studing) his maths when the phone rang.

   | studeying | studying | studeing | studding |
   | ○ | ○ | ○ | ○ |

2. "You are all (wellcome)," said the guide.

   | welcomb | welcom | welcome | wellcom |
   | ○ | ○ | ○ | ○ |

3. Now is not the time to (waist) your savings!

   | waiste | wiaste | waste | waest |
   | ○ | ○ | ○ | ○ |

4. Mum was (sining) the form when her pen ran out of ink.

   | sinning | singing | signning | signing |
   | ○ | ○ | ○ | ○ |

5. When I dropped my ice cream, Mum gave me a (pittiful) look.

   | pityful | pitifull | pitiful | pittifull |
   | ○ | ○ | ○ | ○ |

6. "You will be (tort) a lesson in manners!" warned the driver.

   | tought | taught | torght | targht |
   | ○ | ○ | ○ | ○ |

7. The car was left under a tree in a beachside (avenew).

   | avenue | aveneu | avernue | avinue |
   | ○ | ○ | ○ | ○ |

8. The (noisey) birds were waiting to be fed.

   | noissy | noisy | noisie | niosy |
   | ○ | ○ | ○ | ○ |

9. The coach says he (relackes) after every match.

   | relacks | relaxes | relacxes | rellaxes |
   | ○ | ○ | ○ | ○ |

10. My sister is (equaly) as good at both swimming and diving.

    | eqaully | equalley | equelly | equally |
    | ○ | ○ | ○ | ○ |

11. How do you (compair) two new cars?

    | compar | compaire | compare | compear |
    | ○ | ○ | ○ | ○ |

☞ Answers and explanations on page 179

LANGUAGE CONVENTIONS TEST 4

Look at the labelled drawing. The spelling mistakes on the labels have been circled.
Write the correct spelling of each word in the boxes.

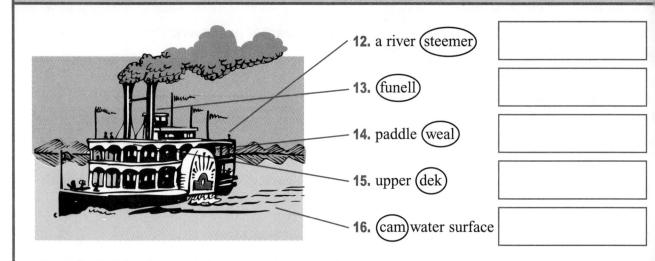

12. a river (steemer)

13. (funell)

14. paddle (weal)

15. upper (dek)

16. (cam) water surface

Read *Speed limits.* Each pair of lines has one word that is incorrect.
Write the correct spelling of each word in the boxes.

Speed limits

17. On the main roads threw town the
speed limit is 60 km per hour. In the

18. bussier parts of the town the limit is
lowered to 50 km per hour. However

19. around schools, at the begining of the school day,
and in afternoons when

20. daily instruction is complete, the limit is
farther reduced to 40 km per hour.

☞ Answers and explanations on page 179

LANGUAGE CONVENTIONS TEST 4

Read the sentences. Each sentence has one word that is incorrect.
Write the correct spelling of each word in the boxes.

21. The baby splashs water all over the bathroom floor.

22. The rearing of turkys in America is big business.

23. Mick was told not to lissen to loud music on his headphones.

24. Is a three-year-old child ready to join a nersury?

25. All cash bonusses of $50 or more will be paid by the end of June.

Colour in the circle with the correct answer.

26. Which word correctly completes this sentence?

Distressing photos of crime ▭▭▭▭ many people feeling sad.

leaves   leaved   leaving   leave
  ○   ○   ○   ○

27. Which word in this sentence should **not** have a capital letter?

"A Bega cheese Factory won first prize for the best soft cheese at the Easter Show.

28. Which word correctly completes this sentence?

I stayed up watching television ▭▭▭▭ I went to sleep.

while   until   because   unless
  ○   ○   ○   ○

29. Which word correctly completes this sentence?

After the assembly ▭▭▭▭ Singh led the class back to their room.

Miss.   miss.   Miss   miss
  ○   ○   ○   ○

☞ Answers and explanations on pages 179–180

30. Which word in this sentence is a pronoun (stands in place of a noun)?

It's a hot day and Richard and I are going to the pool.

It's	day	I	the
○	○	○	○

31. Which sentence has the correct punctuation?

○ Tracy you are always a welcome visitor!

○ Tracy, you are always a welcome visitor.

○ Tracy you are always, a welcome visitor.

○ Tracy you are always a welcome visitor.

32. Which word or words correctly completes this sentence?

I borrowed $10 ▭ my older brother.

off	of	off of	from
○	○	○	○

33. Which title in this sentence should have a full stop?

Capt Gipps invited Mr and Mrs Innes and Dr Hana to her dinner party.

↑ ↑ ↑ ↑
○ ○ ○ ○

34. Which words could be used instead of *ain't* in this sentence?

I ain't going to listen to any more of your rubbish!

are not	will not	is not	am not
○	○	○	○

35. Which sentence has used capital letters correctly?

○ The first day of spring is a Thursday, which was named after Thor, the god of thunder.

○ The first day of Spring is a Thursday, which was named after Thor, the god of thunder.

○ The first day of spring is a Thursday, which was named after Thor, the God of thunder.

○ The first day of Spring is a Thursday, which was named after Thor, the God of thunder.

36. Which letters or word(s) from this sentence should be in brackets ( )?

There is no Goods and Services Tax GST on fresh food, but there is fee if you pay by cheque.

○ Goods and Services Tax

○ GST

○ fresh food

○ fee

37. Which words can all be verbs?

○ lily, silly, baby, copy

○ ski, was, thought, believe

○ above, while, beside, against

○ gymnasium, vacuum, column, volume

38. Which is the correct order for the three missing words?

Leanne's [   ] bedspread was on the laundry floor!

○ old, beautiful, pink

○ beautiful, pink, old

○ beautiful, old, pink

○ pink, old, beautiful

39. Which word or words correctly complete this sentence?

Wolfgang is [   ] of fixing a puncture than Andrew.

capable	more capable	capabler	most capable
○	○	○	○

LANGUAGE CONVENTIONS TEST 4

Read *Guilty*. The text has some gaps.
Choose the correct word(s) and punctuation to fill each gap.

Guilty

40. I looked at Mrs Beatty and she looked at me. I trembled. What would she do to ▊

me.	me?	me?"	Me?
○	○	○	○

41. "You are not allowed in the classroom at ▊ said Mrs Beatty, very seriously. "It's a rule!"

- ○ lunchtime"
- ○ lunchtime.
- ○ lunchtime,"
- ○ lunchtime?"

42. I had a lump in my throat. I ▊ speak, so I nodded foolishly.

- ○ couldnt
- ○ could'nt
- ○ coul'd not
- ○ couldn't

43. Mrs Beatty said with a frozen smile, "I may have to keep you in ▊ I shuddered.

- ○ after school."
- ○ after school".
- ○ after school",
- ○ after school,"

Colour in the circle(s) with the correct answer.

44. Which word or words can be left out of the sentence and still keep the meaning?

Kent was sitting on his bed reading silently to himself without moving his lips.

sitting	on his bed	reading	without moving his lips
○	○	○	○

☞ **Answers and explanations on page 180**

45. Two commas (**,**) have been left out of this sentence.
Where should the missing commas go?

You are in time for a meal but have you eaten Jenny?

46. Which word correctly completes this sentence?

The electrician and his apprentice ▨▨▨▨▨ up until five o'clock each day.

- working
- workers
- work
- works

47. Which word and punctuation correctly completes this sentence?

Tom said, ▨▨▨▨▨ this the way to the office?"

- "is
- "Is?
- "Is
- "is,

48. Which words correctly complete this sentence?

The clock ▨▨▨▨▨ up but it still didn't go for more than an hour.

- had been winded
- was winded
- is been wound
- had been wound

49. Which sentence has the correct punctuation?
- A bright green flashing light, was seen during the eclipse.
- A bright, green flashing light was seen during the eclipse.
- A bright, green, flashing light was seen during the eclipse.
- A bright, green, flashing, light was seen during the eclipse.

50. Which word correctly completes this sentence?

Lester muttered softly, "I don't want ▨▨▨▨▨ of that!"

- nothing
- anything
- none
- any

END OF TEST

Well done! You have completed the final Language Conventions Test. It means that you have answered or attempted more than 200 Language Conventions questions.

How did you go with these test questions? Some were harder than the sample questions. Turn to the next page and mark your work. Check to see where you did well and where you had problems. Make sure you focus on the questions you answered incorrectly or found difficult. Try to understand the explanations given to you and learn from them so you can apply them to other questions—this is how you can improve.

Instructions

- As you check the answer for each question, mark it as correct (✓) or incorrect (✗). Mark any questions that you omitted or left out as incorrect (✗) for the moment.
- Then look at how many you answered correctly in each level.
- You will be able to see what level you are at by finding the point where you started having consistent difficulty with questions. For example, if you answered most questions correctly up to the Intermediate level and then got most questions wrong from then onwards, it is likely your ability is at an Intermediate level. You can ask your parents or teacher to help you do this if it isn't clear to you.

Am I able to ...

	SKILL	ESTIMATED LEVEL	✓ or ✗
1	Add *ing* to a word ending with a consonant and *y*?	Basic	
2	Spell a common two-syllable word often misspelled?	Intermediate	
3	Recognise and spell the correct homonym?	Intermediate	
4	Add *ing* to a word containing a silent *g*?	Intermediate	
5	Add the suffix *ful* to a two-syllable word ending with a consonant and *y*?	Advanced	
6	Recognise and spell a difficult homonym with a less regular letter/sound pattern?	Advanced	
7	Spell a less common word with a French origin?	Intermediate	
8	Add *y* to a one-syllable word ending with *e*?	Intermediate	
9	Add the suffex *es* to a word ending with *x*?	Intermediate	
10	Add the suffix *ly* to a word ending with a single *l*?	Basic	
11	Spell a common two-syllable word with a homonym-type feature?	Advanced	
12	Spell a common two-syllable word?	Basic	
13	Spell a two-syllable word ending with a single *l*?	intermediate	
14	Spell a common word?	Basic	
15	Spell a common word?	Basic	
16	Spell a one-syllable word containing a silent *l*?	Intermediate	
17	Recognise and spell a common *ough* homonym?	Intermediate	
18	Add the suffix *er* to a two-syllable word ending with a consonant and *y*?	Intermediate	
19	Spell a common word with a double letter feature?	Intermediate	
20	Recognise and spell a word often mispronounced?	Advanced	
21	Make a plural of a word ending in *sh*?	Intermediate	
22	Make a plural of a two-syllable word ending with a vowel and *y*?	Intermediate	
23	Recognise and spell a word with a silent *t*?	Advanced	
24	Recognise and spell a common three-syllable word?	Intermediate	
25	Recognise and spell the plural of a less common two-syllable word?	Advanced	
26	Recognise common grammatical conventions for noun–verb agreement?	Intermediate	
27	Recognise a common noun not requiring a capital letter?	Basic	
28	Recognise the appropriate conjunction?	Intermediate	
29	Recognise the correct form of a title?	Basic	

	SKILL	ESTIMATED LEVEL	✓ or ✗
30	Recognise a pronoun in context?	Intermediate	
31	Recognise the position of a comma after the name of a person spoken to?	Intermediate	
32	Recognise the correct preposition for an often misused preposition?	Intermediate	
33	Recognise the correct abbreviation for a title?	Basic	
34	Recognise the correct form of a commonly misused word?	Intermediate	
35	Recognise the correct use of capital letters?	Intermediate	
36	Correctly locate brackets around initials for a place name?	Advanced	
37	Recognise a variety of verbs?	Intermediate	
38	Sequence a series of adjectives correctly?	Advanced	
39	Correctly use adjectives to show comparison?	Intermediate	
40	Complete a sentence with a pronoun and a question mark?	Intermediate	
41	Correctly punctuate a sentence with direct speech?	Advanced	
42	Recognise the correct form of an abbreviation?	Intermediate	
43	Correctly punctuate a sentence with direct speech?	Intermediate	
44	Recognise an example of tautology (redundant word)?	Advanced	
45	Recognise the position of commas to indicate pauses?	Advanced	
46	Recognise common grammatical conventions for noun–verb agreement with a two-person subject?	Intermediate	
47	Correctly place speech marks and a capital letter at the beginning of direct speech?	Advanced	
48	Select a phrase that contains an irregular verb in a past participle?	Advanced	
49	Locate commas in a series of adjectives?	Advanced	
50	Correct a common speech error (double negatives)?	Advanced	

About the test

The NAPLAN Writing test examines a student's ability to write effectively in a specific text type. Students will come across a number of text types at school. We provide you with some graded sample answers on pages 136–138, 143–145 and 149–151.

There is only one Writing question in the NAPLAN Writing Test. You will be provided with some stimulus material that acts as a prompt to writing: something to read or a picture to look at. Your response will be written on supplied paper.

You are told what type of writing will be tested, i.e. what text type it will be. From 2008 to 2010 it was a narrative text and in 2011 it will be a persuasive text.

> Click on the 'Domains' tab on the official NAPLAN website (www.naplan.edu.au) for the latest updates on the Writing Test. A sample Writing Task is also provided.

Marking the Writing Test

When the markers of the NAPLAN Writing Test assess your writing they will mark it according to various criteria. Knowing what they look for will help you understand what to look out for in your own child's writing.

> Click on the 'Domains' tab on the official NAPLAN website (www naplan.edu.au) to see what writing marking criteria NAPLAN markers use when assessing your writing.

The emphasis is on the quality of expression and what the student has to say. Some features that may be emphasised are:

- the quality of the content
- what the student thinks about the topic
- what feelings are developed
- how it is structured
- whether the writing is organised clearly, using paragraphs and appropriate sequencing
- whether the writing is cohesive
- the quality of the spelling and punctuation/ grammar.

Advice for parents and teachers

If students aren't sure how to write a persuasive, narrative or recount text then use the practice tests to develop these skills. It may not be easy for them at first. One way to start is to ask them to talk about the topic and to state their views on the subject. Next you could show them how to plan their writing. Then they can start to write.

Give plenty of praise and encouragement. Remember that Year 4 students are still quite young. Emphasise whatever is good and overlook any errors at first. Space out the time between the writing tasks. Do not attempt one immediately after the other as this does not allow time for development, Come back to these errors at a much later stage, perhaps a little before you start the next practice test.

TIPS FOR WRITING A PERSUASIVE TEXT

Persuasive texts

Persuasive texts (expositions or opinions) are used to 'argue' the case for or against a particular action, plan or point of view—to *persuade* others to see it your way. Persuasive texts need to be well organised and clear so that readers will understand and be convinced by your arguments.

When writing persuasive texts it is best to keep the following points in mind. They will help you get the best possible mark.

Before you start writing

- **Read the question carefully**. You will probably be asked to write your reaction to a particular question or statement, such as *Dogs should be kept out of parks*. Most of the topics that you will be asked to comment on are very general. This means you will probably be writing about something you know and can draw upon your experience. When writing your personal opinion you may include such phrases as *I think, I believe* and *It is important*. Remember to sound confident. Some common ways for the question to be worded are: *Give your opinion on ...; Do you agree or disagree?; What do you think is/are ...?; What changes would you like to see ...?; Is ... a good idea or a bad idea?*

- You will be expected to **give your reasons**. Sometimes the question may actually ask *Give your reasons*. Remember: the stance taken in a persuasive text is not wrong, as long as the writer has evidence to support his or her opinion. How the opinion is supported is as important as the opinion itself.

- Give yourself a few minutes before you start writing to **get your thoughts in order** and jot down points.

The introduction

- Right from the beginning it is important to **let the reader know what position you have taken** or what you believe. You can do this via the title or in the first line or paragraph, which may include a brief preview of the main arguments and some background information.

The body

- **Follow the structure of persuasive texts**. As persuasive texts aim to convince readers, your reasons must be logical and easily understood. You must provide both arguments (points) and evidence to support the arguments.

- **Correctly paragraph your writing**. Use paragraphs with topic sentences to organise your information. Without paragraphs your arguments become confused and difficult to follow. Use one paragraph for each idea or argument. Arguments can be ordered according to your choice. They can be 'numbered', e.g. *firstly, secondly, finally*.

- **Make sure your arguments (or points) are relevant**. They must add to your case. 'Waffle' and unnecessary detail don't improve a persuasive text. It is better to stick to the facts without getting sidetracked. Once you have made a point there is no need to repeat it.

- **Use interesting, precise words**. Include strong persuasive words such as *must, believe, important* or *certainly*. Avoid common words that carry little or no meaning, such as *good*. You can state your arguments using sentences beginning with words such as *firstly, furthermore, finally*.

- **Vary the types and lengths of sentences and the words that begin each sentence**. If your writing includes a personal opinion, try to avoid too many sentences starting with *I*.

- **Use impersonal writing**, although personal opinions can be part of the text.

The conclusion

- The final paragraph must **restate your position** more forcefully and wrap up your case. It can include a recommendation.

When you have finished writing give yourself a few moments to read through your persuasive text. Quickly check spelling and punctuation and insert any words that have been accidentally left out. Direct speech is not a feature of persuasive texts. Indirect speech (reported speech) does not have speech marks (" ").

PERSUASIVE WRITING TESTS

Before you start, read the Tips for writing a persuasive text on page 133.

Today you are going to write a persuasive text, often called an exposition.

Bicycle riding should be taught at school.

What do you think about this idea? Do you support or reject this proposal?

Write to convince a reader of your opinions.

Before you start, read the Tips for writing a persuasive text on page 133.

Discussions are used to look at more than one side of an issue—to look at different points of view. They allow the writer to explore these viewpoints before coming to a decision or conclusion on the issue.

Today you are going to write a persuasive text that is called a discussion.

Nowadays, children get too many costly presents.

What do you think about this idea? Write to provide a reader with the best arguments for and against the proposal. After reading your arguments, the reader should be able to make an informed decision.

Remember: the stance taken in a persuasive text is not wrong, as long as the writer has evidence to support his or her opinion. How the opinion is supported is as important as the opinion itself.

Go to pages 136–138 to see samples of Basic, Intermediate and Advanced levels of writing.

MARKING CHECKLIST FOR PERSUASIVE WRITING TESTS

Use this chart to evaluate your response to Writing Tests 1 and 2. See the glossary on pages 152–155 for an explanation of the terms used.

GUIDELINES FOR WRITING A PERSUASIVE TEXT	✓ or ✗
Focus on general points	
Does the writing make sense?	
Does the writing flow? Are the points logical and relevant?	
Do the points arouse any reactions?	
Do you want to read on—are the arguments engaging and convincing?	
Is the writing style suitable for a persuasive text (objective, and not casual or dismissive)?	
Is the body of the writing mainly in the third person?	
Is the writing assertive, e.g. have you used *is* rather than a less definite term?	
Is the handwriting legible?	

Now focus on the detail. Read each of the following points and find out whether your work has these features.

Focus on content	
Do the opening sentences focus on the topic?	
Is your point of view established early in the writing?	
Is any evidence to support your opinion included?	
Is information relevant to your experiences included?	
Are your points and arguments easy to follow?	
Does your writing follow the format, with an introduction, the body of the text and a conclusion?	
Are your personal opinions included?	
Is the concluding paragraph relevant to the topic?	
Focus on structure, vocabulary, grammar, spelling and punctuation	
Is a variety of correct sentence structures used, including simple, compound and complex sentences?	
Is there a variety of sentence lengths and beginnings?	
Is a new paragraph begun for each additional argument or point?	
Are verbs used correctly with accurate tense and number, e.g. *he is*, *they are*?	
Are adjectives used to improve descriptions, e.g. **obvious** conclusion?	
Are adverbs used to make actions more forceful, e.g. **surely** we must try?	
Is evaluative and emotive language included, e.g. *important*?	
Is a variety of conjunctions used effectively, e.g. *when, because, so, if, but*?	
Are any similes (e.g. *as clear as crystal*) used to stress a point raised?	
Is any other figurative language included: metaphors, exaggeration, rhetorical questions and the occasional exclamation mark, e.g. *That's nonsense!* ?	
Are phrases used such as *I know* and *It is important to*?	
Are approximations avoided such as *probably, perhaps* and *maybe*?	
Is the question referred to in the points raised? (A good way to do this is to use the key words from the question or the introduction.)	
Are connectives used effectively, e.g. *firstly, finally*?	
Are less common words used correctly?	
Is indirect speech used with correct paragraphing, e.g. *many people say*?	
Is punctuation used correctly: capital letters, full stops, commas, exclamation marks and question marks?	
Are common words spelled correctly?	
Are unusual or less common words included?	

Structure

Audience
- The audience is readily identified (bike riders).
- Background information is provided to give context to the points raised.
- A brief statement outlines the issue to be discussed.

Persuasive techniques
- Arguments for the writer's reaction are in separate paragraphs.
- The points raised are obviously important to the writer in a personal way.
- Evidence and examples are used to support the argument.
- Objectivity is maintained throughout the writing.

Text structure
- The text contains a well-organised introduction, body and conclusion.
- The writer refers regularly to words used in the topic.

Paragraphing
- New paragraphs are used for new arguments and a summary.

Cohesion
- The final paragraph establishes where the writer stands on the issue, with a concluding summary of points raised.

Language and ideas

Vocabulary
- A variety of precise verb types is used to establish strong, informed arguments.
- Nouns are used to make generalised statements.
- Well-chosen adverbs and adjectives qualify statements.
- The pronoun *I* is not overused.

Sentence structure
- Sentence beginnings (e.g. *Finally*) are logical.
- Sentence types and lengths are varied.
- A topic sentence introduces each paragraph's main idea.
- Exclamations are used to good effect.

Ideas
- Ideas are balanced well to create a sense of rational, logical argument.
- A strong viewpoint is expressed with a careful choice of words.
- Ideas are presented confidently.

Punctuation
- Punctuation (apostrophes, capital letters and full stops) is correctly applied.

Spelling
- There are no spelling mistakes of common or unusual words.

Basic level—Sample of persuasive writing   Writing Test 1

Bicycle riding should be taught at school

Almost everybody has ridden a bike. Bike riding should be taught at school. It doesn't come naturally. I believe it is just as important as many other activities taught in schools.

It is easy to compare bike riding to swimming. Swimming is taught in schools because it helps to make children safer. Students have lessons and get certificates as they improve. Surely bike riding should be taught for reasons of safety. Roads are getting more dangerous. Students could have lessons at school and progress in a similar way to swimming. Parents would know just how good their bike-riding children are.

Parents are not good teachers of their own children. They can become impatient. The child becomes discouraged. Parents are not familiar with road rules for bike riders. When they rode bikes, things were different!

Finally, if more children were safe bike riders, it could get more cars off the road. Parents wouldn't have to drive their children everywhere if they knew their children were properly trained. There would be less pollution and people would have a cleaner environment. It would help children stay healthy.

I say, teach bike riding at school. It could be a yearly campaign taught in safe conditions, the modern rules can be learned and it will make for healthier children in a cleaner environment.

This writing sample has been analysed based on the marking criteria used by markers to assess the NAPLAN Writing Test.

Intermediate level—Sample of persuasive writing   Writing Test 1

Structure

Audience
- The audience is readily identified (bike riders).
- Background information is provided to give context to the points raised.
- A brief statement outlines the issue to be discussed.

Persuasive techniques
- Arguments for the writer's reaction are in separate paragraphs.
- The points raised are obviously important to the writer in a personal way.
- Evidence and examples are used to support the argument.
- Objectivity is maintained throughout the writing.

Text structure
- The text contains a well-organised introduction, body and conclusion.
- The writer refers regularly to words used in the topic.

Paragraphing
- New paragraphs are used for new arguments and a summary.

Cohesion
- The final paragraph establishes where the writer stands on the issue, with a concluding summary of points raised.

Language and ideas

Vocabulary
- A variety of precise verb types is used to establish strong, informed arguments.
- Nouns are used to make generalised statements.
- Well-chosen adverbs and adjectives qualify statements.
- The pronoun *I* is not overused.

Sentence structure
- Sentence beginnings (e.g. *Finally.*) are logical.
- Sentence types and lengths are varied.
- A topic sentence introduces each paragraph's main idea.
- Exclamations are used to good effect.

Ideas
- Ideas are balanced well to create a sense of rational, logical argument.
- A strong viewpoint is expressed with a careful choice of words.
- Ideas are presented confidently.

Punctuation
- Punctuation (apostrophes, capital letters and stops) is correctly applied.

Spelling
- There are no spelling mistakes of common or unusual words.

Bicycle riding should be taught at school

Almost everybody has ridden a bike. Bike riding should be taught at school. It doesn't come naturally. I believe it is just as important as many other activities taught in schools.

It is easy to compare bike riding to swimming. Swimming is taught in schools because it helps to make children safer in water. Students have lessons and earn certificates as they improve. Surely bike riding should be taught for health and safety reasons. Roads are getting more dangerous. Cars are going faster. Students could have lessons at school and progress in a similar way to swimming. Parents would know just how skilled their bike-riding children are.

Parents are not always the best teachers of their own children. They can become impatient. The child becomes discouraged. Parents are not familiar with road rules for bike riders. When they rode bikes, things were different. Vehicles weren't as big—or as fast!

Finally, if more children were confident bike riders, it could reduce traffic on busy roads. Parents wouldn't have to drive their children everywhere if they knew their children were properly trained. There would be less pollution and people would have a cleaner environment. It would help children stay healthy and fit.

I say, teach bike riding at school. It could be a yearly campaign taught in safe conditions, the modern rules can be learned and it will make for healthier children in a cleaner environment. This is better for everyone.

Riding could become the fourth R!

This writing sample has been analysed based on the marking criteria used by markers to assess the NAPLAN Writing Test.

Language and ideas

Vocabulary
- A variety of precise verb types is used to establish strong, informed arguments.
- Nouns are used to make generalised statements.
- A variety of adverbs and adjectives are well selected to qualify statements.
- The pronoun *I* is not overused.

Sentence structure
- Sentence beginnings (e.g. *Finally*) are logical.
- The types and lengths of sentences vary.
- A topic sentence introduces each paragraph's main idea.
- Exclamations are used to good effect.

Ideas
- Ideas are well balanced to create a sense of rational, logical argument.
- A strong viewpoint is expressed with a careful choice of words.
- Ideas are presented confidently.

Punctuation
- Punctuation (apostrophes, capital letters and full stops) is correctly applied.

Spelling
- There are no spelling mistakes of common or unusual words.

Advanced level—Sample of persuasive writing   Writing Test 1

Bicycle riding should be taught at school

Of course! Almost everybody rides a bike at some time. Bike riding should be taught at school. It's not as if it comes naturally. I believe it is just as important as many other sporting-type activities taught in schools.

It is easy to compare the importance of bike riding to swimming. Swimming is taught in schools because it helps make a safer community. Students have lessons and earn certificates as they progress and improve. Surely bike riding should be taught for health and safety reasons. Everyone recognises that our roads are getting busier and more dangerous. Students could have lessons at school and progress in a similar way. Parents would know just how competent their bike-riding children are.

Parents are not always the best teachers of their children. They can become impatient very quickly. This discourages children from doing their best. Parents are not trained in modern road rules for bike riders. When they learned to ride bikes, they didn't have to wear crash helmets!

Finally, if more children were safe bike riders, it could get more cars off the road. Parents wouldn't have to drive their children everywhere if they knew they were trained and had the skills to handle a bike safely in many different conditions. Bike riding does not burn fossil fuels. There would be less pollution and people would have a cleaner environment. It would also give children an opportunity to remain healthy and stay fit.

Definitely teach bike riding at school. It doesn't have to be every week but as a set campaign once every year. It can be taught in safe conditions, the modern rules can be learned and it will make for healthier children and a cleaner environment.

Riding could become the fourth R!

This writing sample has been analysed based on the marking criteria used by markers to assess the NAPLAN Writing Test.

Structure

Audience
- The audience is readily identified (parents, children).
- Background information is provided to give context to the points raised.
- A brief statement outlines the issue to be discussed.

Persuasive techniques
- Arguments for the writer's reaction are organised into separate paragraphs.
- The points raised are obviously important to the writer in a personal way.
- Evidence and examples are used to support the argument.
- Objectivity is maintained throughout the writing.

Text structure
- The text contains a well-organised introduction, body and conclusion.
- The writer refers regularly to words used in the topic.

Paragraphing
- New paragraphs are used for new arguments and a summary.

Cohesion
- The final paragraphs establish where the writer stands on the issue, with a forceful concluding sentence.

TIPS FOR WRITING A NARRATIVE TEXT

Narrative texts

A **narrative** is a form of prose writing that tells a story. Its main purpose is to entertain. Writers of narratives create experiences that are shared with the reader. To do this the writer uses literary techniques. Such techniques include figurative language (similes, metaphors, alliteration, onomatopoeia, rhetorical questions and repetition), variety in sentence length and type, variety in paragraph length, and direct speech.

In narratives, the author is the person who wrote the story. If the story is in the first person (*I*) we call the character who is telling the story, the narrator.

Give your story vitality by using a variety of sentence beginnings.

Don't forget that your story can include not only the things you or your character might see, but also what you or your character might feel, hear, smell or taste. Remember: there are five senses.

When writing narratives it is best to keep the following points in mind. They will help you get the best possible mark.

Before you start writing

- **Read the question and check the stimulus material carefully.** *Stimulus material* means the topic, title, picture, words, phrases or extract of writing you are given to base your writing on.
- **Write about something you know.** Don't try to write about something way outside your experience.
- Decide if you are going to be writing in the **first person** (you become a character in your story) or in the **third person** (about other characters). When writing in the **first person**, be careful not to overuse the pronoun *I* (e.g. *I did this, I did that*).
- Take a few moments to **jot your ideas down** on a piece of paper. Write down the order in which things happen. These could be the points in your story where you start new paragraphs.
- **Remember: stories have a beginning, middle and end.** It sounds simple but many stories fail because one of these three parts is not well written.

The introduction

- Don't start with *Once upon a time*—this is too **clichéd and predictable**.
- **Don't tell the reader too much in the beginning.** Make the reader want to read on to find out more. The beginning should introduce a problem to be solved.

The body

- **In the middle of your story include events that make solving the problem more difficult or doubtful.** This makes the story interesting.
- **Use a setting that you are familiar with**, e.g. home, school, sport, holiday place, shopping centre. You will then be able to describe the setting realistically.
- **Choose characters that are like people you know** because they are easier to imagine. You don't have to use their real names—it's probably best not to!
- **Use your imagination to make the story more interesting**, but don't try to fill it with weird or disgusting events.
- **Enhance your story with the use of literary techniques**, e.g. similes, metaphors, onomatopoeia and alliteration.
- **Make your paragraphing work for you**. New paragraphs are usually needed for new incidents in your story, changes in time or place, descriptions that move from one sense to another, or changes in the character who is speaking.

The conclusion

- The ending is the hardest part to write because it must have **a connection with the beginning**.
- Never end your stories with: *and it was just a dream; I was saved by a superhero (or by magic); I was dead; and they lived happily ever after!* Endings like these just tell the marker that you don't have a **creative way to end your story**.

When you have finished writing give yourself a few minutes to read through your story. Now is the time to check spelling and punctuation, and to insert words that have been accidentally left out.

There is an old saying: *practice makes perfect.* This applies to writing as much as other skills. Try writing a few short stories before you go into any narrative writing test. Follow these few tips and you will become a better writer.

ALTERNATIVE DESCRIPTIVE WORDS

Make your writing more interesting by using alternatives for these common words.

BIG: large, huge, enormous, gigantic, vast, massive, colossal, immense, bulky, hefty, significant

GOT/GET: obtain, acquire, find, get hold of, gain, achieve, take, retrieve, reach, get back, recover, bring

WENT/GO: leave, reach, go away, depart, exit, move, quit, scramble, crawl, trudge, tread, trample, skip, march, shuffle, swagger, prance, stride, strut

GOOD: decent, enjoyable, superior, fine, excellent, pleasant, lovely, exquisite, brilliant, superb, tremendous

NICE: pleasant, good, kind, polite, fine, lovely

SAW/SEE: glimpse, notice, spot, witness, observe, watch, view, consider, regard, perceive, detect

SMALL: little, minute, short, tiny, miniature, petite, minor, unimportant, microscopic, minuscule, puny

HAPPY: content, pleased, glad, joyful, cheerful, in high spirits, ecstatic, delighted, cheery, jovial, satisfied, thrilled

SAD: depressed, gloomy, miserable, distressed, dismal, disappointed

BAD: awful, terrible, horrific, horrifying, horrendous, evil, naughty, serious, regretful, rotten, appalling, shocking, ghastly, dire, unpleasant, poor, frightening, inexcusable, atrocious, abysmal, sickening, gruesome, unspeakable, outrageous, disgusting, deplorable

GOING: leaving, departing, disappearing, separating, exiting

RUN: sprint, jog, scuttle, scamper, dart, dash, scurry, rush, hurry, trot

WALK: stroll, march, stride, pace, hike, stagger, move, wander, step, tread

SAID:	boasted	exclaimed	mumbled	replied	stammered
acknowledged	boomed	explained	murmured	requested	stated
added	bragged	expressed	nagged	responded	stormed
admitted	called	feared	noted	revealed	stuttered
advised	claimed	giggled	objected	roared	suggested
agreed	commanded	grinned	observed	screamed	taunted
alerted	commented	grunted	ordered	screeched	thought
announced	complained	indicated	pleaded	shouted	told
answered	cried	insisted	pointed out	shrieked	urged
argued	decided	instructed	questioned	snapped	uttered
asked	declared	laughed	rambled	sneered	wailed
babbled	demanded	lied	reassured	sobbed	warned
began	denied	mentioned	remarked	spoke	whined
blurted	emphasised	moaned	repeated	squealed	whispered

NARRATIVE WRITING TESTS

Writing Test 3   Writing a narrative text   40 minutes

**Before you start, read the Tips for writing a narrative text on page 139.
Make sure you look at the Alternative descriptive words on page 140.**

Today you are going to write a narrative or story.

The idea for your story is **a good deed** .

Think about a good deed you have done or have seen.
Good deeds are often of a minor nature. Who was doing
the good deed? What did it involve? Was there any danger
involved? How did the person react to the help provided?
Was the good deed done at home within the family, in a
busy place, or perhaps took place somewhere isolated?

Your story could be about you or someone else. It might
include an animal. How did others react to the incident?
What happened in the end?

Your story might be amusing or it might be serious.
Don't be tempted to make your story unpleasant or gross.

Writing Test 4   Writing a narrative text   40 minutes

**Before you start, read the Tips for writing a narrative text on page 139.
Make sure you look at the Alternative descriptive words on page 140.**

Today you are going to write a narrative or story.

The idea for your story is **in the air** .

Look at the picture on the right. What is the reason there
might be two planes in the air together? Is it a race? Is it a
rescue? Is it a search for something? Think about when and
where your story takes place. Who is involved and how do
they feel? How did others react to the incident?

Your story could be about you or someone else. What happened in the end?

Your story might be amusing or it might be serious. *Don't* be tempted to make your story
unpleasant or gross.

Go to pages 143–145 to see samples of Basic, Intermediate and Advanced levels of writing.

MARKING CHECKLIST FOR NARRATIVE WRITING TESTS

Use this chart to evaluate your response to Writing Tests 3 and 4. See the glossary on pages 152–155 for an explanation of the terms used.

GUIDELINES FOR WRITING A NARRATIVE TEXT	✓ or ✗
Focus on general points	
Does your narrative make sense?	
Does the narrative flow?	
Does the narrative arouse any feelings?	
Do you want to read on, e.g. are the events interesting?	
Is the handwriting legible?	

Now focus on the detail. Read each of the following points and find out whether your work has these features.

Focus on content	
Do the opening sentences 'grab' the reader's interest?	
Is the setting established (i.e. where the action took place)?	
Is the reader told when the action took place?	
Is some information held back to keep the reader intrigued?	
Is it clear who the main character(s) is/are? (The narrative can be in the first person using *I*.)	
Is there a problem to be solved early in the writing?	
Is a complication(s) or unusual event(s) introduced?	
Do descriptions refer to any of the senses, e.g. *cold air*, *strange smell*?	
Is there a climax (a more exciting part near the end)?	
Is the conclusion (resolution of the problem) believable and satisfying?	
Is the meaning and plot clear to create a cohesive believable whole?	
Focus on structure, vocabulary, grammar, spelling and punctuation	
Are a variety of correct sentence structures used, including simple, compound and complex sentences?	
Is there a variety of sentence lengths and beginnings?	
Is a new paragraph begun for changes in time, place or action?	
Have you put conversations or direct speech in separate paragraphs for each change of speaker?	
Have you used verbs correctly with accurate tense and number, e.g. *he is, they are*?	
Are adjectives used to improve descriptions, e.g. **careful** *steps*?	
Are adverbs used to make actions more interesting, e.g. *swam* **strongly**?	
Are adverbs used for time changes (e.g. *later*, *soon*, *then*) and do they create cohesion?	
Is a variety of conjunctions used effectively, e.g. *when, because, so, if, but*?	
Are similes used, e.g. *as clear as glass*?	
Are metaphors used, e.g. *the clouds were dragons in the sky*?	
Are less common words used correctly?	
Is a range of 'said' words used for direct speech, e.g. *ordered, snapped, agreed*?	
Are capital letters used correctly?	
Is punctuation used correctly: full stops, commas, exclamation marks and question marks?	
Are common words spelled correctly?	
Are some unusual or less common words included?	

Language and ideas

Vocabulary
- Adjectives and adverbs are used to enhance the story.
- Verbs are used with skill.
- Conjunctions create a flow to the narrative.
- A variety of 'said' words are used (e.g. *snapped*), which help with characterisation.

Sentence structure
- A variety of sentence beginnings and lengths add interest.
- The story is written in the past tense using the first person.
- The personal pronoun *I* is used correctly and without sounding repetitive.

Ideas
- Interesting detail is included (e.g. *green shopping bag*).
- The writer includes other senses (*noisy*) in the description.

Punctuation
- There are no errors in punctuation.
- Apostrophes and question marks are used correctly.

Spelling
- There are no spelling errors in commonly used or unusual words.

Basic level—Sample of narrative writing   Writing Test 3

A good deed

I was standing in the street when I saw a lady on the next corner. She was watching the cars go up and down. A green shopping bag was in her right hand.

I watched her for a few minutes before I realised she was probably waiting for a break in the traffic to cross the road safely. I suddenly felt sorry for her.

I could do something to help. She might like a helping hand to cross the busy, noisy road.

I walked quickly to the corner and said, "Hello. Are you okay?"

She turned to look at me through her thick glasses. She didn't seem to understand my question so I said it again more slowly. She shook her grey head, not really sure what I was asking, as she looked back to the street. Suddenly the street was quiet. It would be a good chance to guide her across the street.

Gently placing my hand under her elbow I guided her onto the street. The lady was still a bit unsure of what I was doing.

"It's okay," I said, feeling pleased with myself. "We'll cross safely. I'll take my time."

Still she held back as we crossed over. She must have been really scared of the cars.

I helped her up onto the footpath on the opposite side just as another stream of cars dashed by.

"Can I help carry your groceries to your home?" I asked, then added, "Or is there anything else I can do?"

"Yes!" she snapped. "You can help me back across the street. I live on that side!"

Structure

Audience
- The main character is introduced early in the first short paragraph. The reader can relate to a familiar street situation.

Character and setting
- The reader is quickly told what, who, when and where. The title suggests the subject of the story.
- The problem (orientation) is introduced early in the writing—the narrator (*I*) feels a need to offer help.

Text structure
- A series of minor events are related in the order in which they happened.
- The reader has to read on to find out if the narrator was successful.

Paragraphing
- Paragraphs are used to show different time periods and to show when actual words are spoken (direct speech).

Cohesion
- The story has an obvious beginning, middle and end.
- The problem is resolved in an unexpected way with a surprise ending.
- The ending ties in with the title and beginning (the elderly lady didn't require help!).

This writing sample has been analysed based on the marking criteria used by markers to assess the NAPLAN Writing Test.

Structure

Audience
- The main character is introduced early in the first short paragraph. The reader can relate to a familiar street situation.

Character and setting
- The reader is quickly told what, who, when and where. The title suggests the subject of the story.
- The problem (orientation) is introduced early in the writing—the narrator (*I*) feels a need to offer help.

Text structure
- A series of minor events are related in the order in which they happen.
- The reader has to read on to find out if the narrator is successful.

Paragraphing
- Paragraphs are used to show different time periods and to show when actual words are spoken (direct speech).

Cohesion
- The story has an obvious beginning, middle and end.
- The problem is resolved in an unexpected way with a surprise ending.

Language and ideas

Vocabulary
- Adjectives and adverbs are used to enhance the story.
- Verbs are used skilfully.
- Conjunctions create a flow to the narrative.
- A variety of 'said' words are used to create characterisation.

Sentence structure
- A variety of sentence beginnings and lengths add interest.
- The story is written in the past tense using the first person.
- The personal pronoun *I* is used correctly and without sounding repetitive.

Ideas
- Interesting detail is included (e.g. *green shopping bag*).
- The writer includes a sound sense (*noisy*) in the street description.
- Irony is used to provide an amusing ending.
- A simile adds impact.

Punctuation
- There are no errors in punctuation.
- Direct speech is correctly punctuated.
- Exclamations and questions are used to good effect.

Spelling
- There are no spelling errors in commonly used or unusual words.

Intermediate level—Sample of narrative writing   Writing Test 3

A good deed

I was standing in the street when I saw an elderly lady on the next corner. She was patiently watching the cars go up and down. A green shopping bag was in her right hand.

I watched her for a few minutes before I realised she was probably waiting for a break in the traffic to cross the road safely. I suddenly felt sorry for her.

I could do something to help. She might like a helping hand to cross the busy, noisy road.

I walked quickly to the corner and said, "Hello. Are you okay?"

She turned to look at me through her thick glasses. She didn't seem to understand my question so I said it again more slowly. She shook her grey head, not really sure what I was asking, as she looked back to the street. Suddenly the street was quiet. It would be a good chance to guide her across the street.

Gently placing my hand under her elbow I guided her onto the street. The lady was still a bit unsure of what I was doing. She was doubtful about venturing onto the roadway.

"It's okay," I said, feeling pleased with myself. "We'll cross safely. I'll take my time."

Still she resisted a little as we crossed over. She must have been really scared of the cars because I could feel her nervously shaking like a strummed rubber band.

I helped her carefully and calmly up onto the footpath on the opposite side just as another stream of cars dashed by.

"Can I help carry your groceries to your home?" I asked brightly, then added, "Or is there anything else I can do?"

"Yes!" she snapped. "You can help me back across the street. I live on that side!"

This writing sample has been analysed based on the marking criteria used by markers to assess the NAPLAN Writing Test.

Language and ideas

Vocabulary
- Adjectives and adverbs are used to enhance the story.
- Verbs are used skilfully.
- Conjunctions create a flow to the narrative.
- A variety of 'said' words are used to create characterisation.

Sentence structure
- A variety of sentence beginnings and lengths add interest.
- The story is written in the past tense using the first person.
- The personal pronoun *I* is used correctly and without sounding repetitive.

Ideas
- Interesting detail is included (e.g. *heavy green shopping bag*).
- The writer includes a sound sense (*noisy*) in the street description.
- Irony is used to provide an amusing ending.
- Similes add impact.

Punctuation
- There are no errors in punctuation.
- Direct speech is correctly punctuated.
- Exclamations and questions are used to good effect.

Spelling
- There are no spelling errors in commonly used or unusual words.

Structure

Audience
- The main character is introduced early in the first short paragraph. The reader can relate to a familiar street situation.

Character and setting
- The reader is quickly told what, who, when and where. The title suggests the subject of the story.
- The problem (orientation) is introduced early in the writing—the narrator (*I*) feels a need to offer help.

Text structure
- A series of minor events are related in the order in which they happened.
- The reader has to read on to find out if the narrator was successful.

Paragraphing
- Paragraphs are used to show different time periods and to show when actual words are spoken (direct speech).

Cohesion
- The story has an obvious beginning, middle and end.
- The problem is resolved in an unexpected way with a surprise ending.
- The quick ending ties in with the title and beginning (the elderly lady didn't require help!).

Advanced level—Sample of narrative writing   Writing Test 3

A good deed

I was wandering along the street when I saw an elderly lady on the next corner. She was patiently watching the cars zoom up and down. A heavy green shopping bag was hanging in her right hand.

I studied her for a few minutes before I realised she was probably waiting for a break in the traffic to cross the road safely. I suddenly felt sorry for her.

I could do something to help! I could provide a helping hand to cross the busy, noisy road, just like a boy scout.

I walked quickly to the corner and said pleasantly, "Hello. Are you okay? I can help you cross the road."

She turned to look at me oddly through her thick glasses. She didn't seem to understand my question so I said it again more slowly. She shook her grey head, not really sure what I was asking, as she looked back to the street. Suddenly there was a break in the traffic. The street was quiet. It would be a good chance to guide her to the other side.

Gently placing my hand under her elbow I guided her onto the street. The lady was still a bit unsure of what I was doing. She was doubtful about venturing onto the roadway.

"It's okay," I said, feeling a little smug. "We'll cross safely. I'll take my time."

Still she resisted a little as we crossed over. She must have been really scared of the cars because I could feel her nervously shaking like a strummed rubber band.

I helped her carefully and calmly up onto the footpath on the opposite side just as another stream of cars flashed by.

"Can I help carry your groceries to your home?" I asked brightly, then added, "Or is there anything else I can do?"

"Yes!" she snapped unexpectedly. "You can help me back across the street. I live on that side!"

This writing sample has been analysed based on the marking criteria used by markers to assess the NAPLAN Writing Test.

TIPS FOR WRITING AN INFORMATIVE TEXT: RECOUNT

Informative text: recount

A **recount** tells about events that have happened to you or other people. The purpose of a factual recount is to record a series of events in the order they happened and evaluate their importance in some way. A recount can also be fictitious. Whether the recount is factual or fictitious remember to tell who, what, when, where and why. There are many types of recount—diaries, newspaper reports, letters and biographies. Recounts can be the easiest texts to write if you are given the choice. They don't need much planning or organisation as they are a straightforward record of events.

Add interest to your recount by using a variety of sentence beginnings.

Don't forget that your recount can include not only the things you or your character might see, but also what you or your character might feel, hear, smell or taste. Remember: there are five senses.

When writing recounts it is best to keep these points in mind. They will help you get the best possible mark.

Before you start writing

- **Read the question and check the stimulus material carefully.** *Stimulus material* means the topic, title, picture, words, phrases or extract of writing you are given to base your writing on.

- Remember that **a recount is usually told in the past tense** because the events described have already happened.

- **Write about something you know.** Don't try to write about something way outside your experience.

- **Use a setting you are familiar with,** e.g. home, school, sport, holiday place, shopping centre.

- When you have chosen your topic it might be helpful to **jot down a few ideas** quickly on paper so you don't forget them. Make up your mind quickly if you are writing a first-person recount (using *I* as the main character) or a third-person recount. If it is a personal recount, try to avoid too many sentences beginning with *I*.

The introduction

- **A striking title gives impact to a recount.** Newspaper reports do this well.

- The orientation may provide a brief statement about the **who/what/when/where** of the recount. This informs the reader quickly and clearly about the content of the recount.

The body

- **Use conjunctions and connectives** e.g. *when, then, first* or *next*. Because recounts can record either events that happen over a short period or events that happen over a lifetime, you need conjunctions and connectives to link and order the events.

- **Correctly paragraph your writing.** You need a new paragraph when there is a change in time or place or a new idea. You may want to comment on the events as you write about them.

- **Include personal comments**, e.g. about your feelings, your opinions and your reactions but only include comments that add to your recount. 'Waffle' and unnecessary detail don't improve a recount. It is better to stick to the facts without getting sidetracked.

- **Use language imaginatively** so that the recount is interesting, but don't try to fill it with weird or disgusting events.

- **Use figurative language** (similes, metaphors, alliteration, onomatopoeia, rhetorical questions and repetition) when appropriate, but use it in moderation.

The conclusion

- Include a conclusion. This tells how the experience ended. You may give your opinion about what happened and some thoughts you may have had about it. **This final comment on the events or experiences is a way to wrap up your recount.**

When you have finished writing give yourself a few moments to read through your recount. Quickly check spelling and punctuation, and insert words that have been accidentally left out.

There is an old saying: *practice makes perfect*. This applies to writing as much as other skills. Try writing a few short recounts before you go into any recount writing test. Follow these few tips and you will become a better writer.

INFORMATIVE WRITING TESTS

Writing Test 5   Writing an informative text: personal recount   40 minutes

Before you start, read the Tips for writing an informative text on page 146.
Make sure you look at the Alternative descriptive words on page 140.

Today you are going to write a recount about **a friend's birthday party** that you were invited to.

Why were you invited? Where was the party held? How did you get there? What did you do at the party? Was there anything special about the party? Was it a successful party? How did everyone dress and behave?

Writing Test 6   Writing an informative text: factual recount   40 minutes

Before you start, read the Tips for writing an informative text on page 146.
Make sure you look at the Alternative descriptive words on page 140.

Today you are going to write a recount about **a class visit to the town library** .

Pretend that your writing is for the school newsletter. Briefly state the how, when, where and why of your visit. What important events occurred? Was it a successful visit? What difficulties had to be overcome?

Remember: stick to things that could be factual. This is not an opportunity to write a story.

Go to pages 149–151 to see samples of Basic, Intermediate and Advanced levels of writing.

MARKING CHECKLIST FOR INFORMATIVE WRITING TESTS

Use this chart to evaluate your response to Writing Tests 5 and 6.

GUIDELINES FOR WRITING AN INFORMATIVE TEXT	✓ or ✗
Focus on general points	
Does the recount make sense?	
Does the recount flow?	
Does the recount arouse any feelings?	
Do you want to read on, e.g. are the events interesting?	
Is the handwriting legible?	

Now focus on the detail. Read each of the following points and find out whether your work has these features.

Focus on content	
Do the opening sentences introduce the subject of the recount?	
Is the setting established (i.e. when and where the action took place)?	
Is the reader told why the action took place?	
Is it clear who the main character(s) is/are?	
Are the events recorded in chronological (time) order?	
Is the recount in the past tense?	
Are personal pronouns used, e.g. *I*, *we*, *our*?	
Does the writing include some personal comments on the events, e.g. *feeling cold*, *nervous*?	
Do descriptions make any reference to any of the senses, e.g. **loud** commentary, **salty** air?	
Are interesting details included?	
Does the conclusion have a satisfactory summing-up comment?	
Focus on structure, vocabulary, grammar, spelling and punctuation	
Is a variety of correct sentence structures used, including simple, compound and complex sentences?	
Is there a variety of sentence lengths and beginnings?	
Is a new paragraph begun for changes in time, place or action?	
Are subheadings used (optional)?	
Are verbs used correctly with accurate tense and number, e.g. *he is, they are*?	
Are adjectives used to improve descriptions, e.g. **frozen** ground?	
Are adverbs used to make actions more interesting, e.g. swam **strongly**?	
Are adverbs used for time changes (e.g. *later*, *soon*, *then*) and do they create cohesion?	
Is a variety of conjunctions used effectively, e.g. *when, because, so, if, but*?	
Are similes used, e.g. *as clear as glass*?	
Are metaphors used, e.g. *the mountain bike became a bucking horse down the steep slope*?	
Are less common words used correctly?	
Is direct and indirect speech used appropriately with correct paragraphing?	
Are capital letters used correctly?	
Is punctuation correct: full stops, commas, exclamation marks and question marks?	
Is the spelling of common words correct?	
Are some unusual or less common words included?	

Language and ideas

Vocabulary
- Adverbs, verbs and adjectives are well chosen.
- Correctly used personal pronouns (we, I, me) keep the recount flowing.

Sentence structure
- The narrator uses a variety of suitably selected sentence beginnings, including time adverbs (connectives).
- A variety of sentence types and lengths are used.
- There is a controlled use of I as a sentence beginning.

Ideas
- The narrator includes senses other than sight (e.g. cheering).
- A rhetorical question adds to the sense of fun.
- Exclamations are used appropriately.

Punctuation
- Punctuation is well handled.
- A short sentence is used effectively to conclude the recount.
- Capital letters for proper nouns and sentence beginnings are correctly applied.

Spelling
- There are no spelling mistakes in common or unusual words.

Basic level—Sample of informative text: recount writing   Writing Test 5

A friend's birthday party

I got a birthday party invitation from my friend Wanda. I was happy about getting her invitation.

By the time I got to the party I was excited. Lots of kids were running around Wanda's home with streamers and balloons. Others were playing chasing.

Suddenly Wanda's mother clapped her hands. "The jumping castle is ready to go in the backyard!" she called.

For a moment we were all silent, then we dashed, cheering, around the side of the house. There we saw a huge castle. Everyone wanted to have a go. Wanda's mother made sure everyone had a fair turn.

After a while she suggested we play some party games but everyone wanted more goes on the jumping castle.

Later she tried again to have some party games but the jumping castle was too much fun. Why play games when there was a free jumping castle?

Wanda's mother just smiled. She wasn't going to get us off the castle!

Then she called out that the party food was on the table. That did it! Suddenly no-one was jumping.

We didn't go on the castle after eating all that great food, so in the end we played the party games, before going home.

It had been a great party.

Structure

Audience
- The title informs readers of the subject to be recounted.
- The situation is firmly established in the first paragraph.
- The past tense is used.
- The use of the pronoun I indicates that this is a personal recount.

Character and setting
- The who, where and when are established quickly.
- The writer is recounting a familiar subject.

Text structure
- Events happen in order using adverbs of time.
- Precise words are used for details.
- The reader is made aware of the conditions at the time.
- Indirect speech is used correctly.
- The narrator has used a casual, informative style.

Paragraphing
- New paragraphs begin with changes in time.
- New paragraphs are used for a personal reaction.

Cohesion
- A personal comment is used to round off the recount.
- The final sentence refers to the opening sentences.

This writing sample has been analysed based on the marking criteria used by markers to assess the NAPLAN Writing Test.

Language and ideas

Vocabulary
- Adverbs, verbs and adjectives are well chosen.
- The correct use of personal pronouns (*we, I, me*) keeps the recount flowing.

Sentence structure
- The narrator uses a variety of suitably selected sentence beginnings, including time adverbs (connectives).
- The narrator has used a variety of sentence types and lengths.
- There is a controlled use of *I* as a sentence beginning.

Ideas
- The narrator includes senses other than sight (e.g. *cheering*).
- A rhetorical question adds to the sense of fun.
- Exclamations are used appropriately.

Punctuation
- Punctuation is well handled.
- A short exclamation is used effectively to conclude the recount.
- Capital letters for proper nouns and sentence beginnings are correctly applied.

Spelling
- There are no spelling mistakes in common or unusual words.

Intermediate level—Sample of informative text: recount writing   Writing Test 5

A friend's birthday party

On Wednesday I found a letter for me among the mail for Mum and Dad. It was a birthday party invitation from my friend Wanda. I was pretty happy about the invitation.

I wasn't the first to arrive and by the time I got to the party I was excited. There were lots of kids running around Wanda's home with streamers and balloons. Some were shouting and others were playing a noisy game of chasing.

Suddenly Wanda's mother clapped her hands and called, "The jumping castle is pumped up and ready to go in the backyard!"

For a moment we were all silent, then we dashed, cheering, around the side of the house. We discovered a huge castle. All the kids wanted to have a go. Wanda's mother made sure everyone had a fair turn.

After a while she suggested we play some party games but everyone wanted more goes on the jumping castle.

Later she tried again to have some party games but the jumping castle was too much fun. Why play games when there was a jumping castle for free?

Wanda's mother just smiled. She wasn't going to get us away from the castle!

Then she called out that party food was on the table. That did it! Instantly no-one was jumping.

It was not a good idea to go on the castle after eating all that great food, so in the end we played the party games before going home.

I had a fun time!

Structure

Audience
- The title informs readers of the subject to be recounted.
- The situation is firmly established in the first paragraph.
- The past tense is used.
- The use of the pronoun *I* indicates that this is a personal recount.

Character and setting
- The who, where and when are established quickly.
- The writer is recounting a familiar subject.

Text structure
- Events happen in order using adverbs of time.
- Precise words are used for details.
- The reader is made aware of the conditions at the time.
- Indirect speech is used correctly.
- The narrator has used a casual, informative style.

Paragraphing
- New paragraphs begin with changes in time.
- New paragraphs are used for a personal reaction.

Cohesion
- A personal comment is used to round off the recount.
- The final sentence refers to the opening sentences.

This writing sample has been analysed based on the marking criteria used by markers to assess the NAPLAN Writing Test.

Language and ideas

Vocabulary
- Adverbs, adjectives and verbs are well chosen.
- The correct use of personal pronouns (*we, I, me*) keeps the recount flowing.

Sentence structure
- The narrator uses a variety of suitably selected sentence beginnings, including time adverbs (connectives).
- A variety of sentence types and lengths has been used.
- There is a controlled use of *as* a sentence beginning.

Ideas
- A rhetorical question adds to the sense of fun.
- Exclamations are used appropriately.
- The narrator includes senses other than sight (e.g. *cheering, yummy*).
- A simile adds impact to the recount.

Punctuation
- Punctuation is well handled.
- Capital letters are correctly applied.
- A short exclamation is used effectively to conclude the recount.

Spelling
- There are no spelling mistakes in common or unusual words.

Structure

Audience
- The title informs readers of the subject to be recounted.
- The situation is firmly established in the first paragraph.
- The past tense is used.
- The use of the pronoun *I* indicates that this is a personal recount.

Character and setting
- The who, where and when are established quickly.
- The writer is recounting a familiar subject.

Text structure
- Events happen in order using adverbs of time.
- Precise words are used for details.
- The reader is made aware of the conditions at the time.
- Indirect speech is used correctly.
- The narrator has used a casual, informative style.

Paragraphing
- New paragraphs begin with changes in time.
- New paragraphs are used for a personal reaction.

Cohesion
- A personal comment is used to round off the recount.
- The final sentences refer to the opening sentences.

Advanced level—Sample of informative text: recount writing   Writing Test 5

A friend's birthday party

On Wednesday I found a letter for me amongst the mail for Mum and Dad. It was a birthday party invitation from my friend Wanda—and it was for next Saturday. I was pretty happy about getting her invitation.

By the time I got to the party I was excited. I wasn't the first to arrive. There were lots of kids running around Wanda's home with streamers and balloons. Some were shouting and others were playing a noisy game of chasing.

Suddenly Wanda's mother appeared and clapped her hands. "The jumping castle is pumped up and ready to go in the backyard!" she called.

For a moment we were all silent then we dashed, cheering, around the side of the house. There, in one corner, was a huge castle. All the kids wanted to have a go. Wanda's mother made sure everyone had a fair turn.

After a while she suggested we play some party games but everyone wanted more goes on the jumping castle.

Later she tried again to have some party games but the jumping castle was too much fun. Why play games when there was a jumping castle for free?

Wanda's mother just smiled. She wasn't going to get us away from the castle! Then she called out that the party food was on the table. That did it! Instantly, no one was jumping. The castle was as deserted as a ghost town.

It was not a good idea to go on the castle after eating all that yummy food, so in the end we played the party games, before finally going home.

It was a great party. I had had a fun time!

This writing sample has been analysed based on the marking criteria used by markers to assess the NAPLAN Writing Test.

GLOSSARY OF GRAMMAR AND PUNCTUATION TERMS

Adjectival clause

An adjectival clause provides further information about the person or thing named. It functions as an adjective, describing a noun and answering the questions What? Who? How many? or Which?

This is the bike that was given to me by Dad.

An adjectival clause contains a subject and verb and usually begins with a relative pronoun (*who, whom, whose, which* or *that*).

Adjectival phrase

An adjectival phrase is a group of words, usually beginning with a preposition or a participle, that acts as an adjective, giving more information about a noun.

The man in the blue jumper is my uncle. (preposition)
The man wearing the blue jumper is my uncle. (participle)

Adjective

An adjective is a word used to describe and give more information about a noun.

Some examples include *multiple* books, *a delicious* cake, *my gorgeous* friend.

Adverb

An adverb is a word used to describe or give more information about a verb, an adjective or another adverb, to tell us how, when or where the action happened. Adverbs often end in *-ly*.

The flag flapped wildly in the wind. (how)
I always brush my teeth in the morning. (when)
He slid downwards towards the side of the boat. (where)

Adverbial clause

An adverbial clause acts like an adverb. It functions as an adverb, giving more information about the verb, usually telling when, where or how. It indicates manner, place or time, condition, reason, purpose or result.

Water is important because plant and animal communities depend on water for food, water and shelter. (reason)

Adverbial phrase

An adverbial phrase is a group of words, usually beginning with a preposition, that acts as an adverb, giving more information about the time, manner or place of the verb, telling us where, when, how far, how long, with what, with whom, and about what.

Chloe hit Ava with the old broom.

Apostrophe

An apostrophe is a form of punctuation used to show:

1. a contraction (missing letters in a word), e.g. *can't = cannot*

2. possession, e.g. *David's book, the boys'* (plural) *mother*

Brackets ( )

Brackets are a form of punctuation used to include an explanatory word, phrase or sentence.

He took the book from his friend (Anthony) but never returned it.

Capital letter

Capital letters are used at the beginning of sentences, as well as for proper nouns, e.g. the names of people, places, titles, countries and days of the week.

Colon (:)

A colon is a form of punctuation used to introduce information, such as a list, or further information to explain the sentence.

The following should be taken on the trip: a warm jacket, socks, jeans, shirts and shoes.
The warning read: "Give up now or else!"

Comma (,)

A comma is a form of punctuation used to break up the parts of a sentence, or to separate words or phrases in a list.

The children, who have not completed their homework, will be punished.

My brother likes to eat peanuts, steaks, oranges and cherries.

Conjunction/connective

A conjunction or connective is a word joining parts of a sentence or whole sentences.

Conjunctions: *and, but, where, wherever, after, since, whenever, before, while, until, as, by, like, as if, though, because, so that, in order to, if, unless, in case, although, despite, whereas, even though*

My button fell off <u>because</u> it was not sewn on properly.

Connectives: *in other words, for example, therefore, then, next, previously, finally, firstly, to conclude, in that case, however, despite this, otherwise*

<u>First</u> we do our homework, and <u>then</u> we go out to play.

Dash (—)

A dash is a form of punctuation used to indicate a break or pause in a sentence.

Life is like giving a concert while you are learning to play the instrument—now that is really living.

We really hoped that he would stay—maybe next time.

Exclamation mark (!)

An exclamation mark is a form of punctuation used to mark the end of a sentence where strong emotions or reactions are expressed.

Ouch! I cut my finger.

I listened at the door. Nothing!

Full stop (.)

A full stop is a form of punctuation used to indicate the end of a sentence. Full stops are used before the closing of speech marks.

David sat under the tree.

Nicholas said, "Come with me, James."

Imagery

Imagery includes:

Metaphor is when one thing is compared to another by referring to it as *being* something else, e.g. *The thief looked at her <u>with a vulture's eye</u>.*

Simile is comparing two different things using the words *as* or *like*, e.g. *The hail pelted down <u>like bullets</u>. He was <u>as brave as a lion</u>.*

Personification is giving human qualities or characteristics to non-human things, e.g. *<u>Trees were dancing</u> in the wind.*

Alliteration is the repetition of consonant sounds at the beginning of successive words for effect, e.g. *The <u>sun sizzled softly</u> on the sand. The <u>rising river rushed</u>.*

Onomatopoeia is the formation of words to imitate the sound a certain thing or action might make, e.g. *banged, crashed, hissed, sizzled.*

Repetition is repeating words or phrases for effect, e.g. *Indeed there will be time, time to relax, time to enjoy the sun and surf, time to be oneself once more.*

Modality

Modality is the range of words used to express different degrees of probability, inclination or obligation. Modality can be expressed in a number of ways:

- Verbs: *can, could, should, might, must, will, it seems, it appears*
- Adverbs: *perhaps, possibly, generally, presumably, apparently, sometimes, always, never, undoubtedly, certainly, absolutely, definitely*
- Nouns: *possibility, opportunity, necessity*
- Adjectives: *possible, promising, expected, likely, probable.*

Noun

Nouns are words used to represent a person, place or thing. There are different types of nouns:

Common nouns are nouns that represent things in general, e.g. *boy, desk, bike.*

Proper nouns take a capital letter. They represent a particular thing, rather than just a general thing. Proper nouns are used to name a place, person, title, day of the week, month and city/country, e.g. *Michaela, November, Monday, Madagascar.*

Abstract nouns are things we cannot see but can often feel, e.g. *sadness, honesty, pride, love, hate, issue, advantages.*

Collective nouns are nouns that name a group of things, e.g. *herd, litter, team, flock.*

Preposition

Prepositions are words that connect a noun or pronoun to another word in the sentence. They also indicate time, space, manner or circumstance.

I am sitting between my brother and sister.

Some common prepositions are *in, at, on, to, by, into, onto, inside, out, under, below, before, after, from, since, during, until, after, off, above, over, across, among, around, beside, between, down, past, near, through, without.*

Pronoun

A pronoun is a word that is used in place of a noun. Pronouns refer to something that has already been named, e.g. *My brother is 10 years old. He is taller than me.*

Be careful of repetition and ambiguous use of pronouns: *He went to the shops with his friend and he told him to wait outside.*

The pronouns are *I, you, me, he, she, it, we, they, mine, yours, his, hers, ours, theirs, myself, ourselves, herself, himself, themselves, yourself, this, that, these, those, each, any, some, all, one, who, which, what, whose, whom.*

Question mark (?)

Question marks are needed at the end of any sentence that asks something, e.g. *What did you say?*

If a question is asked in an indirect way it does not have a question mark, e.g. *I asked him what he said.*

Speech (quotation) marks (" ")

Speech (quotation) marks have several uses.

- They are used to show the exact words of the speaker:

  John said, "I prefer the colour blue."

  "What are you doing?" asked Marie.

  "I like cats," said Sophia, "but I like dogs too."

  When there is more than one speaker, a new line should be used when the new person begins to speak:

  "What should we do now?" asked Ellen.

  "I'm not too sure," whispered Jonathan.

- They can be used when writing the names of books and movies (italic can also be used for this purpose).

- They are used when quoting exact words or phrases from a text.

Semicolon (;)

A semicolon is a form of punctuation used to separate clauses. It is stronger than a comma but not as final as a full stop.

Eighteen people started on the team; only twelve remain.

In our class we have people from Melbourne, Victoria; Sydney, New South Wales; and Brisbane, Queensland.

Sentence

A sentence is a group of words consisting of one or more clauses. It will begin with a capital letter and end with a full stop, question mark or exclamation mark.

Simple sentence: *I caught the bus.*

Compound sentence: *I caught the bus and arrived at school on time.*

Complex sentence: *Since I managed to get up early, I caught the bus.*

Tense

Tense is the form of the verb (a doing word) that tells us when something is happening in time—present, past or future.

I look, I am looking (present)

I will look (future)

I looked, I was looking (past)

Auxiliary verbs (e.g. *be*, *have* and *do*) help change the verb to express time, e.g. *I have looked, I have been looking, I had looked, I had been looking, I will have looked, I will have been looking.*

Verb

A verb is a word that expresses an action, e.g. I *ran*, he *forgot*, she *went*, Mary *shouted*. It can also express a state, e.g. *the boys are laughing, he is clever, he was all smiles, I know my spelling words.*

Active verb: The verb is in the active voice when the subject of the sentence does the action, e.g. *James broke the glass.* (*James* is the subject of this sentence.)

Passive verb: The passive voice tells you what happens to or what is being done to the subject, e.g. *The glass was broken by James.* (Here *the glass* is the subject of the sentence.)

The passive is often used in informative writing, where it is not always necessary to state the doer of an action, or the doer is not known, or it is not relevant.

ANSWERS TO NUMERACY TESTS

NUMERACY TEST 1 (pp. 25–29)

1. **4.** 2 piles of 6 means 2 times 6 is 12. Jack has 12 matchboxes, which is 4 boxes if arranged in 3 piles.

2. **quarter to 4.** As half an hour is 30 minutes, then 30 minutes added to 3:15 is 3:45, or quarter to four.

3. **18 km.** 3 times 6 is 18 which means that Thomas runs a total of 18 km.

4. **5 × 8 − 8.** Try each of the choices to find that the right answer is 5 × 8 − 8 which means 40 minus 8 is 32.

5. **$35.** The difference is 44 (Ethan) minus 9 (Kai). This is 44 − 9 which is 35.

6. **1090.** 9 hundred and 90 plus another 1 hundred is 10 hundred and 90, or 1090.

7. **20 March.** The Tuesdays are 6, 13, 20 and 27 March.

8. **9.** 22 take away 10 is 12 and then take another 3 away to leave 9.

9. Craig can draw six triangles in a shape. 2 out of 6 shaded is the same as 1 out of 3 or a third.

10. **24.** The pattern is a difference of 6. This means 42 − 6 = 36, then 36 − 6 = 30 and finally 30 − 6 = 24.

11. **203.** 1827 ÷ 9 = 203. Take care to include the 0 because 9 into 18 is 2, 9 into 2 is 0 and 9 into 27 is 3.

12.

13. **17.** The number pattern is 3, 5, 7, 9, 11, 13, 15, 17, … The 8th number in this pattern is 17.

14. **280 067.** Two hundred and eighty thousand is 280 000 and sixty-seven is 67. This gives the answer 280 067.

15. **8.** 48 ÷ 6 is 8, which means Billy bought 8 tickets.

16. **76 410.** The largest possible number is formed using the digits in order from highest to lowest.

17. **78.** Double 38 gives 76 and then adding 2 gives 78.

18. **South.** Clockwise is the way the hands move around an analog watch.

    Anti-clockwise is the other way, and a quarter-turn moves from West to South.

19. **65.** Start with 45 and add 5 to make 50, then 60 to make 110. This means that you have added a total of 65.

20. **3100.** The order is 799, 3018, 3100, 4029, 4198. The middle number is 3100.

21. **35 km.** Jamil drives 9 km from Princeton to the City and then 26 km from the City to Sterling. Add 26 and 9 to get the total kilometres he drove: 35 km.

22. **$35.** Prawn cocktail is about $10, Chicken about $20 and Sundae about $5. As 10 + 20 + 5 is 35, Josie's meal will cost about $35.

23. 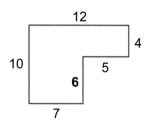 This shape does not have a line of symmetry.

24. **44 cm.**

Adding the numbers gives 44.

25. **8 and 9.** First units, 11 minus 2 is 9, and in the tens column, 8 becomes 7 minus 4 is 3. This means 81 − 42 = 39.

26. **hexagon.** The pentagon has the numbers 5, 10, 15. This means the hexagon is 19th.

27. **56.** Check all the different possible pairs and 56 is the only one that is a multiple of 7 (56 = 8 × 7).

28. **$1.70.** First, $5.00 minus $1.60 is $3.40 which is the cost of the 2 pens. As half of $3.40 is $1.70, the cost of 1 pen is $1.70.

29. **16.** Two rows of 10 gives 20 squares. Now, four-fifths is 4 out of 5, or 8 out of 10, or 16 out of 20. This means that 16 squares will be shaded.

30. **70 cents.** Adding 60 (for the cheese sandwich) and 70 (for the bottle of water) gives 130, or $1.30. The change from $2 is 70 cents.

31. The green is the largest section on the spinner and blue and red are equally sized sections.

32. $15. As 1 dozen is 12, then 2 dozen is 24. Now 24 ÷ 8 = 3 which means that 3 bags of bread rolls need to be bought. As 3 times 5 is 15 then the cost will be $15.

33. C. The party starts at 10:30. Adding 2 hours gives 12:30 and then another half an hour gives 1:00.

34. $11. As 2 lots of 6 is 12, then the mandarines will cost $8 (2 x $4) and the 2 cucumbers will cost $3 (2 x $1.50). The total cost is $11 ($8 + $3).

35. 2, 1, 1, 1. First, the total cost of one of each item is $4.20. This means that David still has another 80 cents and so David can buy another pen.

NUMERACY TEST 2 (pp. 33–38)

1. $6. As 18 minus 12 is 6, then Lizzie has $6.

2. 13 years old. Owen is older than 12 but younger than 15. From the choices, Owen could be 13.

3. Each triangle is half a square which means that 2 triangles equals a square. There are 10 triangles which make 5 squares plus the other 5 squares make 10 squares.

4. 9. Carrie scored 12 and Jonathon scored 3 so the difference is 12 − 3 = 9.

5. 12. Friday has 4 marks and Saturday has 8 so the sum is 8 + 4 = 12.

6. 8. 4 edges on the square base plus 4 sloping edges. The total is 8.

7.

From $27.50 add **50c** to $28, then **$2** gives $30 and then **$10** gives $40.

8. 15. Add 9 plus 6 to get the larger number of 15.

9. 30 mm. To add 16 and 14, first add 16 to 10 to give 26 and then another 4 is 30.

10. 120. 95 plus 5 is 100 and then another 20 is 120.

11. 1932. Grandma was born in the year 2000 minus 68. Now, 100 − 68 is the same as 100 − 60 − 8 which is 40 − 8 and equals 32. This means the year is 1932.

12. 16. The number pattern is 4, 7, 10, 13, 16, … The 5th number in this pattern is 16 so Figure 5 would have 16 matchsticks.

13. 8:35. From 8:15 another 20 minutes is 8:35.

14. 6 and 7. The column heading is 6 because multiples of 6 are below it. The row heading is 7 as multiples of 7 are to its right.

15. 12 and 20. First 28 minus 4 is 24. There are 3 jumps so each jump will be 24 ÷ 3 is 8. Now, adding gives 4, 12, 20, 28. The missing numbers are 12 and 20.

16. 100. First, 500 minus 200 is 300. This means the 3 discs have a total mass of 300 grams, so that each disc has a mass of 100 grams.

17. 86 cm. As 1 metre is 100 cm, you have to subtract 14 from 100. Now, 100 − 14 is the same as 90 − 4, which is 86.

18. 2. The number pattern is counting on by 15. This means the pattern is 15, 30, 45, 60, 75, 90, … As 75 and 90 are listed, then there are 2 numbers shown.

19. 24. There are 4 pentagons on each sheet. As 6 times 4 is 24, then Magda has 24 pentagon stickers.

20. $1.30. It is easiest to add the coins with the largest value first. Now $2 + $1 + 50c + 10c + 5c + 5c is $3.70. This means an additional $1.30 is needed.

21. 8. There are 15 cards on the table. Steve picks up 7 cards: 12, 18, 27, 9, 15, 21, 6. This leaves 8 cards on the table.

22. Year 4 has raised four times as much as Year 5. Year 4 raised $480 which is 4 times $120.

23.

24. 1.2. The number line is divided into tenths (or 0.1s) so that the arrow is pointing to 1.2.

25. **1 unit = 15 km.** The map shows 3 units represents 45 km. Divide by 3 to work out that 1 unit represents 15 km.

26. **7.** First, < means 'is less than'. As 16 + 5 is 21, then the question is 21 is less than 4 times 'what number'? This means the number can be any number such as 6, 7, 8 and so on. From the choices, the only answer can be 7.

27. **100.** For every 3 girls there are 5 boys. If you multiply both numbers by 20 then for every 60 girls there are 100 boys.

28. **D.** A is opposite C, and B is opposite the blank. This means that D is opposite the face with 3 dots and so D will have 4 dots.

29. **13.** 8 boys and 5 girls means a total of 13 students had eaten cereal.

30. **7.** Dividing 46 by 6 gives 7 with 4 left over. This means that Rianna used 7 bags.

31. **16.** 3 lots of 4 and 2 lots of 2 equals 12 plus 4 which is 16. This means that there were 16 customers.

32. This bag has more white balls than black balls.

33. **Louise.** First, Breanna is D, Tamara is B, Kimberley must be A and Louise must be C.

34. **50 cm.** Each square has a side length of 5 cm. By counting, the perimeter is 50 cm.

35. **7.**

This cube here

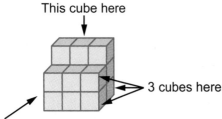

3 cubes here

Another 3 cubes on this side

NUMERACY TEST 3 (pp. 41–46)

1. **Tuesday.** There were 5 students absent on Tuesday which was the largest total.

2. **65 cents.** To $2.35 add 5 cents to get $2.40 then another 60 cents to make $3.00. This means a total of 65 cents.

3. There is only one axis of symmetry.

4. **27 February.** The Sundays are on 6, 13, 20 and 27 February. This means the last Sunday is 27 February.

5. A pentagon has five sides.

6. By counting, this shape has an area of 11 square units which is greater than any other shape.

7.

8. **6 × 3.** Each tricycle has 3 wheels. This means that 6 tricycles have 6 times 3 wheels, or 6 × 3.

9. **609.** This is the closest number as it is only 9 away from 600.

10. **6.** Divide 30 by 5 to get 6 teams.

11. **30.** Adding 9 + 3 + 6 + 4 + 8 equals 30.

12. **2.**

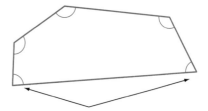

These angles are less than 90 degrees.

13. **4.** The factors of 8 are 1, 2, 4, 8. This means that 4 numbers are factors.

14. **There were more boys on the bus than women**. There are 9 boys and 4 women on the bus.

15. **6 and 2.** In the units column, the missing number is 2 as 4 plus 2 is 6. In the tens column, 5 plus 7 is 12, and in the hundreds column, the carried 1 plus 2 and 3 is 6. This means the missing numbers are 6 and 2.

16. **30.** You are looking for a number between 20 and 40 that can be divided by 5 and 6. The only possible number is 30.

17. four thousand. 304 816 is three hundred and four thousand, eight hundred and sixteen.

18. $10^2 + 3 > 12^2$. Remember $>$ means 'is greater than' and 10^2 is $10 \times 10 = 100$.

Here you have $103 > 144$ which is not true.

19. Jannah. Ross's birthday is in January. As March is the next month on the list then Jannah's birthday is next.

20. 2 and 3. Shape 2 is a pentagonal prism and Shape 3 is a hexagonal pyramid and both have 7 faces.

21. 27 years. Buffy's mother is $4 \times 9 = 36$ and her grandmother is $7 \times 9 = 63$. The age difference is $63 - 36 = 27$ years.

22. 27 cm. The wall is 3 rows high and so the height is 3 times 9 which is 27 cm.

23. Bill gives Ben 4 stickers. Bill has 8 more stickers than Ben. If he gives 4 to Ben it will mean that both boys have 20 stickers each.

24. 220. You need to find 260 minus 40. By leaving the 0s off the end you have 26 minus 4 which is 22. Now, by putting the 0s back in, the answer is 220.

25. seventh. You can draw a little picture using **B** for Brody, **K** for Kirstie and Xs for everyone else:

Front: X **B** X X X X **K**

You can see that Kirstie is seventh in line.

26.

One of the three columns is black. This means one-third.

27. 5 degrees. You just use $8 - 3$ which is 5. The rest of the numbers in the question are just information about the time of day.

28. 3 out of 8. There are 3 hearts out of the 8 cards.

29. 10. All the other choices are possible: 7 (3 and 4), 8 (2 and 6) and 11 (5 and 6).

30. 29 375. As 31 thousand minus 2 thousand is 29 thousand, so the answer is 29 375.

31. 8. Each pie is cut into 2 halves. This means the 4 pies are cut into 8 halves.

32. 4. There must be 4 teams because 4 lots of 12 is 48 which is close to the 50 players.

33. Beads. When Laura leaves the Phone shop the first store on her right is the Camera shop and the second on her right is the Beads shop.

34. Multiply by 3 and then subtract 1. Checking the choices, this is the only option that works: 2 times 3 minus 1 is 5; 5 times 3 minus 1 is 14; and 14 times 3 minus 1 is 41.

35. 22 minutes. 7 minutes gets to 4:00 and then another 15 to reach 4:15. The total time is found by adding 7 and 15 which is 22 minutes.

36. 4. 14 divided by 4 is 3 with a remainder of 2. This means that Joanna needs to buy 4 packets of batteries.

37. 96. When we times 32 by 3 the answer is 96.

38. 5180.

$$\begin{array}{r} 4870 \\ + \quad 310 \\ \hline 5180 \end{array}$$

39. 10. Garth used 6 out of 12 stickers and has another 6 remaining. Gavin used 2 out of the 6 which leaves 4 remaining. The total is 6 plus 4 which is 10.

40. B. 18 out of 36 students, or half of the students, travel by car. This means car travellers is A. A quarter ride, so that is D. Bus is larger than walkers, so bus travellers are B.

NUMERACY TEST 4 (pp. 49–54)

1. $14 \div 7 = 2$. The number of weeks is found by dividing.

2. rectangle.

3. 11. From the graph 5 students liked Netball and 6 liked Hockey, so the total is 11.

4. $18 \div 2 < 13$. This is the only true number sentence as 9 is less than 13.

5. 3. $1.49 is close to $1.50. As 3 lots of $1.50 is $4.50, 3 avocados can be bought.

6. 4. Marnee watched 5 and Kim watched 1. The difference is 4 so Marnee watched 4 more movies than Kim.

7. 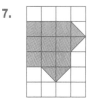 This shape has an area of 11 square units as there are 9 squares and 4 triangles which make up 2 more squares.

8. **very likely.** There are 5 odd numbers out of the 6, so it is very likely that an odd number is chosen.

9. **5, 9, 13, 17, …** Start with 5 and then add 4 gives 9, then add 4 gives 13, and so on.

10.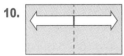

11. **34.** Add the numbers in the Received column: 6 + 9 + 10 + 9 equals 34.

12. **37.** For 54 − 17, first 54 minus 10 is 44 and then take away another 7 gives 37.

13. **pentagonal prism.** The net has 2 pentagons and 5 squares.

14.

15. **26 mm.**

16. **2.**

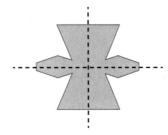

17. **87 km.** The total distance is found by adding the two distances. 48 + 39 is 48 plus 40 minus 1 which is 87 km.

18. **Brett.** Keith leaves his home and turns left into Bridges Road. He turns right into Sublime Road and passes Brett's house.

19. The chance of choosing a black ball is two in four (or a half) which is more than the chance of choosing a black ball from the other three cans.

20. **6 + 0.8 + 0.07.** 6.87 is 6 ones + 8 tenths + 7 hundredths.

21. **10:55.** 5 minutes before 11 is written as 10:55.

22. **7 and 7.** For the units, 2 plus 5 is 7. For the tens, 'what number' plus 6 is 13 which means the number is 7.

23. There is no card with the number 2 in the bag.

24. **5.** She will need to buy 5 bags because 5 lots of 6 is 30. If she bought 4 she would only have 24 buns which is not enough.

25. **$150.** You need to find 960 minus 810. You can forget the 0s and make the question easier: 96 minus 81 is 15. Putting the 0s back gives 150.

26. **very likely.** Three out of five of the cards match Mary's card. This means that it is very likely that she will have a match.

27. **27 litres.** The tank is a little more than half full. As half of 50 is 25, than there is about 27 litres.

28. **20.** Each of the 6 pots has 3 seeds which is 18 seeds. Add the 2 extra seeds which means a total of 20 seeds.

29. **12.** There are 5 numbers already crossed out. For factors of 18, Lionel crosses out the 3, 6, 9, 18. For the factors of 20, Lionel crosses out the 5, 10, 20. This is a total of 12 numbers crossed out.

30. $\frac{1}{2}$. If 6 children share 3 apples, then 2 children share 1 apple. This means that each child receives half an apple.

31. **2 and 6.** In the units column 13 minus 7 is 6, and in the tens column, 4 becomes 3 so 3 minus 'a number' is 1. That number is 2.

32. **three-eighths.** There are 3 out of 8 petals that are shaded.

33. **1360.** To change from multiplying by 8 to multiplying by 80, just put a 0 on the end of the answer. The 136 becomes 1360.

34. **7.** The numbers in the triangles are the multiples of 3. This means that the numbers in the circle but not in the triangle are even numbers that are not multiples of 3. These are 2, 4, 8, 10, 14, 16, 20. There are 7 numbers.

35. **$12.** First, 24 divided by 6 is 4. This means that Con pays for 4 lots of $3 which is $12.

36. **9.** There are 12 squares. One-quarter of 12 is 12 ÷ 4 which is 3. If 3 squares are shaded then 9 squares are not shaded.

37. **24 cm.** The tallest student is 152 cm and the shortest is 128 cm. The difference is 152 − 128 which is 52 − 28 which is 32 − 8. The answer is 24 cm.

38. 4. 12 bean plants need 3 sticks each which means 36 sticks. This means that the gardener needs to buy 4 packets.

39. D. The number line has been divided into eighths. This means that D is pointing to seven-eighths.

40. 58 cm.

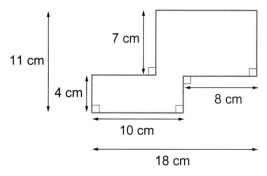

The shape is 18 cm wide and 11 cm high.

This means the perimeter can be found by adding 18, 18, 11 and 11. This is a total of 58 cm.

READING TEST 1 (pp. 57–65)

1. **Greenhood orchids keep a supply of water in their root system.**

   This is a **fact-finding type of question**. The answer is a fact in the text. You read that *They store water in a tuber (a type of bulb)* (see lines 25–26).

2. **droughts.**

   This is a **fact-finding type of question**. The answer is a fact in the text. You read that *wild goats are a threat* (see line 36) and *The spread of towns and land clearing for farms mean that the places where it grows naturally are disappearing* (see lines 31–34).

3. **It would be a shame if greenhood orchids become extinct.**

   This is a **judgement type of question**. You have to distinguish between facts given in the text and what someone thinks. An opinion is how someone feels about something. The word *shame* is a hint that this option is an opinion because it is expressing a judgement about something that could happen.

4. **The plant called asparagus fern is not a fern.**

   This is a **language type of question**. To find the answer you have to read the text carefully, especially the section that is quoted: *Weeds spreading into bushland, such as the so-called asparagus fern* (see lines 40–41). *So-called* implies that it is incorrectly named.

5. **A breeze will make the flowers sway on their long stems.**

   This is an **inferring type of question**. To find the answer you have to 'read between the lines'. You read *It has a stem about 40 centimetres long, which may carry a number of green flowers. The hood-like flowers are about 2 centimetres long* (see lines 8–11). As the stems are so long, the breeze will make the small flowers nod or sway.

6. **The flowers look like green leaves.**

   This is a **fact-finding type of question**. The answer is a fact in the text. You read that *Because greenhoods are small and the flowers look like leaves, they easily go unnoticed in the bush* (see lines 17–19).

7. **The library was about to close.**

This is a **fact-finding type of question**. The answer is a fact in the text. You read that *'You have less than 20 minutes. Then I close the doors,' said Mr Stone* (see lines 7–8).

8. **nervous.**

This is an **inferring type of question**. To find the answer you have to 'read between the lines'. You read *As Alicia pulled a book off the shelf other books tumbled to the floor. Holly looked around guiltily* (see lines 16–18). They were getting flustered. The library was about to close and they needed to put the books back on the shelf. You also read *the more they hurried the more they fumbled around* (see lines 20–21). They were feeling nervous.

9. **panicky.**

This is an **inferring type of question**. To find the answer you have to 'read between the lines'. You read *'How do we get out?' hissed Alicia* (see line 29). You also read *'Do you remember how to get to the front desk?' asked Alicia urgently* (see lines 31–32). The words *hissed* and *urgently* indicate that Alicia is desperate to find out how to get out of the library. She is panicky.

10. **(1, 3, 2, 4)**

This is a **fact-finding type of question**. The answer is a fact in the text. By reading the text carefully you will identify the correct order of events. 1. The girls entered the library to get a book for Alicia. 2. The warning bell rang. 3. Alicia knocked some books off the shelf. 4. The library lights went off.

11. **was not confident she knew the answer.**

This is an **inferring type of question**. To find the answer you have to 'read between the lines'. You read *Holly nodded, then shook her head. 'It could be this way* (see lines 33–34). The word *could* means she isn't sure that she knows the way.

12. **She was helping Alicia because it was her first day at the school.**

This is a **fact-finding type of question**. The answer is a fact in the text. You read *After Alicia's first day at her new school Holly took her back to the library* (see lines 1–2).

13. **They might have upset Mr Stone by spilling his books.**

This is an **inferring type of question**. To find the answer you have to 'read between the lines'. You read *As Alicia pulled a book off the shelf other books tumbled to the floor. Holly looked around guiltily* (see lines 16–18). You also read *'They have to be in order or … '* (see lines 23–24). Combine this information with your own knowledge of libraries that the books have to be on the shelves and in the correct order. Holly knows knocking the books off the shelves could get them into trouble.

14. **and don't cost the student any money.**

This is an **inferring type of question**. To find the answer you have to 'read between the lines'. By reading the poster and looking at the pictures you can work out that all the activities have no real cost involved for the participant (e.g. reading a book). As they do not involve costs you can infer that the activities are easy to do *and* don't involve the outlay of money.

15. **type of recycling.**

This is an **inferring type of question**. To find the answer you have to 'read between the lines'. You read *Making craft objects out of used things* (see lines 3–4) and in the picture you can see that the girl is making something out of an old coat hanger instead of throwing it away. As recycling is creating new objects from old ones you can work out that making craft objects out of used material is a type of recycling.

16. **energy.**

This is a **fact-finding type of question**. The answer is a fact in the text. You read that *The aim in schools is to raise awareness about energy and make savings in energy* (see lines 13–14).

17. **Remember to turn off lights.**

This is a **judgement type of question**. You can see that all the activities are fairly simple. Combine it with your own knowledge of the activities and you will see that switching off lights requires only the flick of a switch and saves money as well as energy. All the other activities require more time or effort.

18. **is a day for the whole world to observe.**

This is a **language type of question**. To find the answer you have to read the text carefully, especially the section that is quoted: *It is a global day for people to think about protecting the earth* (see lines 11–12). Combine this information with your own knowledge of the word *global* which means anything relating to the globe we live on—the Earth. Then you can work out that a global day is a day for the whole world to observe.

19. a recount.

This is a **synthesis type of question**. To find the answer you have to read the whole text. The text is about what happened on a special day at school. Then combine this information with your knowledge of text types to work out that this text is a *recount* as it recounts (tells in order) the events of the day in the order in which they happened.

20. provide mental and physical relaxation.

This is a **fact-finding type of question**. The answer is a fact in the text. You read that *Yoga is a combination of breathing exercises, physical postures and meditation* (see lines 8–10). You also read *It is a way of keeping fit and healthy* (see line 12).

21. making a healthy fruit drink.

This is a **fact-finding type of question**. The answer is a fact not directly stated in the text. You read that *The next activity was fun. We were shown how to make healthy fruit drinks* (see lines 36–37). No other activity had such a positive reaction.

22. the smoking video.

This is an **inferring type of question**. To find the answer you have to 'read between the lines'. You read *After recess we watched a video about smoking and lung cancer. Some of the things that go into cigarettes are disgusting. Worse than that were the pictures of what cancer does to the human body. Why people smoke I'll never know!* (see lines 30–35). Combine this with your own knowledge of the negative effects of smoking and the narrator's negative reaction, which is emphasised by the use of an exclamation mark, and you can conclude that the narrator found the video most upsetting.

23. Healthy lifestyle.

This is **a synthesis type of question**. To find the answer you have to read the whole text. You read that the students learned about *yoga and meditation* (see lines 5–6), *preventing skin cancer* (see lines 25–26), *how to make healthy fruit drinks* (see line 37) and *trying out something you have never done before* (see lines 48–49). The text is about having and keeping a healthy body and

feeling content with oneself. Of the options the most suitable title is *Healthy lifestyle*.

24. loud cry.

This is a **language type of question**. To find the answer you have to read the poem carefully, especially the section that is quoted: *The cat-er-wauling ... wakes the neighbour's dogs in fright* (see lines 5–6). If it wakes the dog in fright then that suggests that *caterwauling* is a loud cry. You may already know that *caterwauling* means 'a cat's howl or screech'—the poet has hyphenated the word to humorously emphasise the syllable *cat*.

25. badly behaved.

This is an **inferring type of question**. To find the answer you have to 'read between the lines'. You read that Geronimo *scratches ... the polished floor* (see line 3) and later *A goldfish dead upon the floor / Scooped from its tank* (see lines 7–8). Combine this with your own knowledge that the things that Geronimo is doing such as eating pet fish and scratching the floor are not the actions of a well-behaved cat and you can conclude that Geronimo is a badly behaved cat.

26. The poet feels something drastic has to be done.

This is an **inferring type of question**. To find the answer you have to 'read between the lines'. You read that the cat has caused *A cat-a-logue of feline crime* (see line 2) and *A cat-a-strophic tale of woe* (see line 15) and you read about all the crimes he has committed such as a dead goldfish, muddy pawprints and a broken vase. The poet is implying that the cat is a criminal. As criminals are usually arrested you can work out that the poet feels something drastic has to be done. You can also work this out by eliminating the wrong options. There is no suggestion that the cat could pay for the damage or is endangering the poet's life, or that the poet doesn't like cats.

27. The list goes on for hours and hours.

This is a **fact-finding type of question**. The answer is a fact in the text. You read about some of the things the cat does—*scratches on the polished floor* (see line 3), *A goldfish dead* (see line 7), *Mum's broken vase* (see line 9) and so on—but there is not enough time to list them all. This is an obvious exaggeration to make a point.

28. keep the poem cheerful and amusing.

This is a **language type of question**. To find the answer you have to read the text carefully, especially the sections that are quoted: *cat-a-logue* (see line 2), *cat-er-wauling* (see line 5) and *cat-a-strophic* (see line 15). These are puns and puns are meant to amuse.

29. safe use.

This is an **inferring type of question**. To find the answer you have to 'read between the lines'. You read *Inhalers are used by people to treat or control breathing complaints* (see lines 1–2) and *When you inhale a dose you are breathing in the actual dose required* (see lines 3–4). The text is not talking about emergency situations only, or the use of inhalers only after being washed. As the inhaler ensures that people with breathing complaints get the right dose it follows that they are designed for safe use.

30. chemist shop.

This is an **inferring type of question**. To find the answer you have to 'read between the lines'. You read *Inhalers are used by people to treat or control breathing complaints* (see lines 1–2). Combine this information with your own knowledge that medicines are obtained from chemists and you can work out that both inhalers and instructions for their use would most likely be available at a chemist shop.

31. instructions.

This is a **language type of question**. To find the answer you have to read the text carefully, especially the heading, and then look at the layout of the text. You read *If you follow these instructions, most inhalers are simple to use* (see lines 12–14). *Directions* is a synonym for *instructions*. Both words mean 'how to do something'.

32. They don't give an exact dosage of the medicine.

This is a **fact-finding type of question**. The answer is a fact in the text. You read *Aerosol sprays do not have the same precise control of the dosage* (see lines 4–6).

33. twisted to the right.

This is a **fact-finding type of question**. The answer is a fact in the text. You read *1. Remove the cap. 2. Twist the grip to the right* (see lines 15–16).

34. when it clicks after being twisted.

This is a **fact-finding type of question**. The answer is a fact in the text. You read *twist the grip back again (to the left) until it clicks. The inhaler is now loaded with a measured dose* (see lines 18–22).

35. it is always the same exact amount.

This is a **language type of question**. To find the answer you have to read the text carefully, especially the section that is quoted: *The inhaler is now loaded with a measured dose* (see lines 21–22). You also read *When you inhale a dose you are breathing in the actual dose size required* (see lines 3–4). This implies there is no guesswork involved. Combine this information with your own knowledge of how the device controls the dosage, as if it has been carefully measured.

READING TEST 2
(pp. 67–74)

1. persuade people to visit Happy Hoot.

This is a **synthesis type of question**. To find the answer you have to read the whole text. You read *A full day's fun for the whole family* (see line 1). You also read *It's a great day out* (see line 2). The advertisement presents all the positive aspects of the park. It is designed to persuade people to go to the park and spend money.

2. enjoyable excitement.

This is a **language type of question**. To find the answer you have to read the text carefully, especially the section that is quoted: *The Happy Hoot Fun Park* (see line 2). The word *Hoot* is linked with *Happy* and *Fun*. When you look at the picture you will see that everyone is enjoying themselves. Combine this information with your own knowledge of how you would feel if you went to the park for a day's activities to work out that *Hoot* in this advertisement means 'enjoyable excitement'.

3. physical.

This is an **inferring type of question**. To find the answer you have to 'read between the lines'. You read the list of activities are all physical activities such as *toboggan run* and *mini-golf* (see lines 6 and 9). The picture shows you that most of the activities are sporting-type activities so you can work out that most of the activities at Happy Hoot are physical.

4. **family picnics.**

   This is a **fact-finding type of question**. The answer is a fact in the text. You read *shaded picnic areas by the creek* (see line 11). The advertisement has a picture of a family picnic next to the creek.

5. **speed karts.**

   This is a **fact-finding type of question**. The answer is a fact in the text. You read *fully enclosed footwear [is] essential for [speed karts]* (see line 8).

6. **under three years of age.**

   This is a **fact-finding type of question**. The answer is a fact in the text. You read that *Children under three years are admitted free to the park … Parental supervision required* (see lines 15 and 17).

7. **use private cars.**

   This is a **fact-finding type of question**. The answer is a fact in the text. You read that to get to the park visitors must travel *45 minutes south of Willang on the Forest Hwy* (see line 15).

8. **pink.**

   This is a **fact-finding type of question**. The answer is a fact in the text. You read that *My snowman was turning pink* (see line 1) and *Our snowman was white again. But it didn't last. Slowly the pink seeped through* (see lines 19–21).

9. **naked.**

   This is a **fact-finding type of question**. The answer is a fact in the text. You read that the snowman said *'I'm so hot and embarrassed'* (see line 37–38) and *'I don't have any clothes on'* (see line 41).

10. **Jasper had a bright idea.**

    This is a **language type of question**. To find the answer you have to read the text carefully, especially the section that is quoted: *'I'm sure I saw a light bulb pop out of his head!'* (see lines 13–14). The quote is an example of idiom. An idiom is not meant to be taken literally. To say someone had a light bulb go off means that they had a bright idea. Crystal meant that Jasper looked as if he was getting a bright idea.

11. **for a short while.**

    This is an **inferring type of question**. To find the answer you have to 'read between the lines'. You read *Our snowman was white again. But it didn't last. Slowly the pink seeped through* (see lines 19–21). The word *Slowly* implies that it took a short while for the pink to seep through and for Jasper and Crystal's feeling of satisfaction to last.

12. **self-conscious.**

    This is an **inferring type of question**. To find the answer you have to 'read between the lines'. You read the snowman says *'I'm so hot and embarrassed I might melt'* (see lines 37–38). He is not wearing any clothes. He has hung his head. Combine this with your own knowledge of the meaning of *self-conscious* (conscious of how people are looking at oneself) to work out that the snowman is feeling self-conscious.

13. **(2, 3, 1, 4).**

    This is a **fact-finding type of question**. The answer is a fact in the text. By reading the text carefully you will identify the correct order of events. 1. Crystal rushes over to Jasper's house. 2. Jasper and Crystal pack snow onto the snowman. 3. The snowman's cheeks start burning. 4. The snowman admits why he felt embarrassed.

14. **full of very comical events.**

    This is an **inferring type of question**. To find the answer you have to 'read between the lines'. You read that the reviewer *giggled while reading it, and my children did too* (see lines 10–12). Combine this with your own knowledge that people giggle because they find something funny and you will understand that the book is full of comical (amusing) events.

15. **Lewis Ridge.**

    This is a **fact-finding type of question**. The answer is a fact in the text. You read that the book was *illustrated by Lewis Ridge* (see lines 14–15). The information is also on the book's cover.

16. **keep readers engrossed in the stories.**

    This is a **language type of question**. To find the answer you have to read the text carefully, especially the section that is quoted: *I review many books and only a few I describe as 'un-put-downable'. It's not so much that you can't* *put down* Mouse for a Month, *as that you lose track of all time. The reader is totally swept up by the weird events* (see lines 1–10). The term is an example of idiom. An idiom is not meant to be taken literally. It means that the reader is so interested in the *weird events* that he or she doesn't want to stop reading.

17. **He decided mice were pleasant creatures**.

This is a **fact-finding type of question**. The answer is a fact in the text. You read that *My dislike of small furry things [mice] has changed* (see lines 37–38).

18. **mischievous.**

This is an **inferring type of question**. To find the answer you have to 'read between the lines'. You read *The kids want him to be the class pet and plan to take turns to look after him. It turns out that Nicky has schemes of his own* (see lines 26–28). You also read the book is about *Nicky's wild (mis)adventures* (see line 41). If Nicky doesn't want to do what the kids want but has his own schemes, it suggests he is mischievous. Both the words *schemes* and *misadventures* suggest an element of mischief and his name (Nicky is a bit like Micky) also suggests that he might be mischievous.

19. **It has large print on uncrowded pages.**

This is an **inferring type of question**. To find the answer you have to 'read between the lines'. You read it has *more white space and larger print than chapter books for older readers* (see lines 17–19). Combine this with your own knowledge that books for young children have a lot of white space and large print to work out that the book is suitable for younger readers.

20. **factual report.**

This is a **synthesis type of question**. To work out the answer you have to read the whole text to determine what its purpose is. You read facts on where and how large Antarctica is, about its ice, wind and temperature. The text does not provide personal, technical or scientific details. It is a factual report.

21. **high winds.**

This is a **fact-finding type of question**. The answer is a fact in the text. You read that on the mountains *The rock is exposed to winds so strong for most of the year that snow or ice cannot take hold* (see lines 31–33).

22. **More fresh water is stored in Antarctica than on any other continent.**

This is a **fact-finding type of question.** The answer is a fact in the text. You read that *Antarctica contains about 70% of the world's fresh water* (see lines 9–11). No other continent could contain as much water as Antarctica as only 30% of fresh water remains.

23. **5 kilometres.**

This is a **fact-finding type of question**. The answer is a fact in the text. You read that the *ice is generally 2.5 kilometres deep (2500 metres) but in places it is 5 kilometres deep* (see lines 7–9).

24. **ground snow stirred up by wild winds.**

This is a **fact-finding type of question**. The answer is a fact in the text. You read that *Pictures of explorers caught in snowstorms only give part of the truth. It is the windiest place on Earth. Much of the snow and ice is whipped up off the ground by ferocious winds* (see lines 18–22).

25. **protection from the winds.**

This is a **judgement type of question**. You read *It [Antarctica] is the windiest place on Earth* (see lines 19–20). Combine it with your own knowledge of how ferocious winds can make the temperature feel even colder to work out that protection from the wind would be important to survive in Antarctica.

26. **fantasy.**

This is a **synthesis type of question**. To find the answer you have to read the whole text. The text is about what makes up a fairy tale. There is a range of different ideas in the text. These include stating that fairy tales include *magic, spells and enchantment* (see lines 8–9), talking animals (see line 12) and *far-fetched events* (see lines 10–11). Combine this information with your own knowledge that a fantasy is a fiction about imaginary worlds and supernatural events to work out that a fairy tale is a type of fantasy.

27. **Fairy tales were not always written down.**

This is a **fact-finding type of question**. The answer is a fact in the text. You read that *Fairy tales were once part of oral storytelling* (see lines 38–39) and *The Brothers Grimm were the first writers [of fairy tales]* (see line 42). All other options are opinions. They are what some people may think or believe.

ANSWERS TO READING TESTS

28. **a description of their looks or what they are.**

This is a **fact-finding type of question**. The answer is a fact in the text. You read that *Their characters are often nameless; they represent people—and animals* (see lines 16–17).

29. **recorded tales that had been told but not written down.**

This is an **inferring type of question**. To find the answer you have to 'read between the lines'. You read *Fairy tales were once part of oral storytelling* (see lines 38–39) and *The Brothers Grimm were the first writers who aimed to collect and preserve the stories in a book* (see lines 42–44). If the tales had not been recorded by the Brothers Grimm they may have been lost forever.

30. **Fairy tales began as spoken stories.**

This is a **fact-finding type of question**. The answer is a fact in the text. You read that *Fairy tales were once part of oral storytelling* (see lines 38–39).

31. **hope.**

This is an **inferring type of question**. To find the answer you have to 'read between the lines'. You read *Good people generally win through or are rewarded—and everyone lives happily ever after* (see lines 21–23). This gives people, no matter how badly off, hope that things can improve.

32. **a lack of concern.**

This is an **inferring type of question**. To find the answer you have to 'read between the lines'. You can see that the doctor is more worried about the smelly armpit than he is about the footballer's injury. He has a lack of concern for the discomfort of others.

33. **that the player has head injuries.**

This is an **inferring type of question**. To find the answer you have to 'read between the lines'. You can see that the injured player is 'seeing' stars. This is a cartoonist's technique to suggest head injuries, such as concussion.

34. **the doctor is more worried about the smell than the injury.**

This is an **inferring type of question**. To find the answer you have to 'read between the lines'. You can see that the doctor is not paying attention to a serious injury but is more concerned about the less important armpit smell.

35. **Doctor to the rescue!**

This is an **inferring type of question**. To find the answer you have to 'read between the lines'. You can see that the doctor is not really 'coming to the rescue'. The exclamation mark suggests that this is a really fun caption for the cartoon.

READING TEST 3 (pp. 76–84)

1. **lies told by parents.**

This is an **inferring type of question**. To find the answer you have to 'read between the lines'. You read that *It all started with … Let's say, it started with the tooth fairy* (see lines 27–28). You also read *Parents will become stressed if they find that you have read the book* (see lines 9–10) and *There are people (you can guess who) who want you to believe that a fairy … flies around … planking coins into glasses* (see lines 29–33). The story goes on to show that stories told to children are lies.

2. **parents.**

This is an **inferring type of question**. To find the answer you have to 'read between the lines'. You read *There are people (you can guess who) who want you to believe that a fairy … [plonks] coins into glasses of fresh water* (see lines 29–33). Combine this information with your own knowledge of the things parents tell their children such as *if you are naughty the bogyman will get you* (see lines 43–44) and about the tooth fairy. Another hint that *you can guess who* refers to parents is the sentence *Parents will become stressed if they find that you have read the book* (see lines 9–10).

3. **in a book that might get banned.**

This is a **fact-finding type of question**. The answer is a fact in the text. You read *that this information may soon be banned. It is from my book* The Grand Hoax (see lines 3–5).

4. **reveals made-up stories parents tell their children.**

This is a **synthesis type of question**. To find the answer you have to read the whole text. The text is about the stories parents tell their children. They talk about tooth fairies and Easter bunnies (see lines 29–35 and 39–41). You then combine these ideas with the fact that they do not really exist. They are part of *The Grand Hoax*. A hoax is an act intended to trick people into believing something that is not real.

5. **He thinks he has convinced readers.**

   This is an **inferring type of question**. To find the answer you have to 'read between the lines'. The writer has given several examples to prove there is a hoax—you read *What about slimy frogs that turn into handsome princes* (see lines 36–37) and *What about that Easter rabbit* (see line 39). Lastly, you read *Of course, if you are naughty the bogyman will get you. Need I go on?* (see lines 43–44). He or she doesn't believe any more proof needs to be presented. The question is a rhetorical question, which is one that doesn't require an answer.

6. **an amusing explanation.**

   This is a **synthesis type of question**. To find the answer you have to read the whole text. The text is written with a 'tongue-in-cheek style' which implies the writer isn't really serious about his or her complaint. A lot of unnecessary exaggeration is used to make the point: *Read on, at the risk of having all those beliefs you hold dear to your pure, little heart shattered. Smashed. Exploded. Devastated. Wiped clean from the memory card in your hard-drive brain. Evaporated in a puff of disbelief. Vanished. Into thin air* (see lines 14–19). He is being amusing.

7. **English children.**

   This is a **fact-finding type of question**. The answer is a fact in the text. You read that *Wooden hoop races for English boys and girls were popular in the 1800s* (see lines 26–27).

8. **for training to become a hunter.**

   This is a **fact-finding type of question**. The answer is a fact in the text. You read that *Hoops were important to Native American boys in target practice games ... This was good training for when they became hunters* (see lines 7–19).

9. **practical.**

   This is a **synthesis type of question**. To find the answer you have to read the whole text. The text is about how hoops have been used in different cultures across different times. You read *The ancient Greeks played with them to keep fit and healthy* (see lines 2–3) and Native

Americans used hoops as *good training for when they became hunters* (see lines 18–19). You also read about more modern times when *Doctors encouraged hoop activities as exercise* (see lines 42–43). Most of the uses of hoops listed in the passage were practical.

10. **They were used by children of different heights.**

    This is a **fact-finding type of question**. The answer is a fact in the text. You read that *Hoops were made to suit the contestant's size* (see lines 27–28).

11. **They were made from wood in the 1800s, not plastic.**

    This is a **fact-finding type of question**. The answer is a fact in the text. You read that *Wooden hoop races for English boys and girls were popular in the 1800s* (see lines 26–27) and *In the 1960s a hoop craze swept many countries ... The hoop, often called a hula-hoop, was a lightweight, tubular plastic hoop* (see lines 32–36).

12. **to show how hoops have changed over time.**

    This is a **synthesis type of question**. To find the answer you have to read the whole text. The text is about how hoops have changed over time and how their use has varied. You read *The ancient Greeks played with them to keep fit and healthy ... as far back as 300 BC* (see lines 2–6) and *In the 1960s a hoop craze swept many countries* when people twirled *brightly coloured, plastic hoops* (see lines 32–40) and *Modern Olympic Games gymnasts have used hoops, as well as ribbons and balls, as props in some gymnastic events* (see lines 45–49).

13. **Mercury is about the same size as our moon.**

    This is a **fact-finding type of question**. The answer is a fact in the text. You read that Mercury *is a battered and baked planet slightly larger than the Earth's moon* (see lines 2–3).

14. **59 Earth days.**

    This is a **fact-finding type of question**. The answer is a fact in the text. You read *One Mercury day lasts about 59 Earth days* (see line 33).

15. **more mountainous than Earth's landform.**

    This is an **inferring type of question**. To find the answer you have to 'read between the lines'. You read *The cliffs on Mercury are up to 2 kilometres high, and stretch for hundreds* *of kilometres* (**see lines 28–29**). You also read of a crater that *is 1300 kilometres wide* (**see line 23**). Combine this information with your own knowledge that Earth does not have that many mountains and craters so that Mercury must be more mountainous than Earth.

16. the tilt of the planet.

This is a **fact-finding type of question**. The answer is a fact in the text. You read that *sunlight never touches some valley shadows due to the planet's tilt* (**see lines 5–7**).

17. its craters.

This is an **inferring type of question**. To find the answer you have to 'read between the lines'. You read that Mercury *is covered in craters* (**see lines 3–4**) and that one crater *is 1300 kilometres wide* (**see lines 22–23**) and *another large crater, is 643 kilometres across* (**see line 27**). From this you can work out that the craters are the most spectacular feature of Mercury's landscape.

18. the photographs showed things scientists don't understand.

This is a **language type of question**. To find the answer you have to read the text carefully, especially the section that is quoted *Although the first series of fly-pasts answered many questions, it has raised others* (**see lines 47–49**). Combine this information with your own knowledge of how this implies that the new information brought with it more unexplained features.

19. a weather implement.

This is a **fact-finding type of question**. The answer is a fact in the text. You read that *Windsocks … are weather instruments* (**see lines 4–5**). *Instrument* has a similar meaning to *implement*.

20. let the wind blow through.

This is a **fact-finding type of question**. The answer is a fact in the text. You read that *The wind can blow straight through* (**see line 9**). If the wind could not blow through, the sock would fill up with air and not do what it was intended to do.

21. at a railway station.

This is an **inferring type of question**. To find the answer you have to 'read between the lines'. You read that windsocks are important on *roads or on high bridges* (**see line 23**) or *at airports on high poles* (**see lines 12–13**). Cars,

caravans and planes are affected by wind conditions. Trains, in contrast, are heavy and run on rails so are not affected by the wind. You can therefore work out that windsocks would be of little use at a railway station.

22. the speed of the wind.

This is a **fact-finding type of question**. The answer is a fact in the text. You read that *When the wind is strong, windsocks stick straight out* (**see lines 27–28**) and *in a light breeze windsocks … hang down at an angle* (**see lines 28–30**). The diagram also indicates this point.

23. they are lit up.

This is a **fact-finding type of question**. The answer is a fact in the text. You read that pilots need to *know about the wind as they land or take off* (**see lines 13–14**). You also read *At night they are lit up* (**see lines 14–15**).

24. green.

This is a **fact-finding type of question**. The answer is a fact in the text. You read that *His … green scales fell like rain* (**see lines 30–31**). You know that scales cover the outside of animals so Puff was a green dragon.

25. cheerful.

This is a **judgement type of question**. You read Puff *frolicked in the autumn mist* (**see line 9**) and that he was a *rascal* (**see line 4**). Jackie Paper and Puff spent a lot of time playing imaginary characters. Combine it with your own knowledge of how small children play with imaginary friends and you can work out that Puff was a cheerful (imaginary) dragon.

26. an imaginary friend.

This is an **inferring type of question**. To find the answer you have to 'read between the lines'. You read that Puff and Jackie Paper *would travel on a boat with billowed sail / Jackie kept a lookout perched on Puff's gigantic tail* (**see lines 14–17**). This couldn't really happen. The game is all make-believe for Jackie Paper. Combine this with your own knowledge that dragons don't exist to work out that Puff is Jackie's imaginary friend.

27. childhood doesn't last forever.

This is a **synthesis type of question**. To find the answer you have to read all of the song's lyrics. The song is about what happens when children grow up. They lose interest in childish things. You read *One grey night it happened, Jackie Paper came no more / And Puff that mighty dragon, he ceased his fearless roar* (see lines 26–29). This implies that the imaginary world of childhood comes to an end for everybody.

28. **got older and found new interests.**

    This is an **inferring type of question**. To find the answer you have to 'read between the lines'. You read *Jackie Paper came no more / And Puff, that mighty dragon, he ceased his fearless roar* (see lines 26–29) This implies that Jackie Paper had found more grown-up things to interest him. You also read *Puff that mighty dragon, sadly slipped into his cave* (see lines 36–37). He was no longer required for imaginary adventures.

29. **description.**

    This is a **synthesis type of question**. To work out the answer you have to read the whole text to determine what the purpose of the text is. It is a description of the guesthouse and its surroundings.

30. **The house was in an isolated place.**

    This is an **inferring type of question**. To find the answer you have to 'read between the lines'. You read that *from the kitchen he (Michael) could partly see the old wooden bridge* (see lines 15–17) and from another window he could see *across the river flats* (see line 22). You also read *Cattle could be heard lowing some way off* (see lines 48–49) and that Michael felt lonely, all of which imply that the house was in an isolated position.

31. **basic.**

    This is an **inferring type of question**. To find the answer you have to 'read between the lines'. You read *It's a bit primitive* (see line 5), that the kitchen had a *basic sink cupboard* (see line 21) and the *bed lamp perched on a milk crate* (see lines 44–45) and *the pattern on the [table] top had almost worn off* (lines 31–32). All the facilities are described as very basic.

32. **The house may have had changes but it was not all that modern.**

    This is a **language type of question**. To find the answer you have to read the text carefully, especially the section that is quoted: *It's been, ahh, modernised a couple of times* (see lines 4–5). Paul's hesitation in describing

the cottage as *modernised* is indicated by the word *ahh*. The facilities of the cottage are all described as basic so he is using *modernised* euphemistically to make the cottage appear more acceptable.

33. **The furniture in the room took up too much space to allow the door to open.**

    This is a **fact-finding type of question**. The answer is a fact in the text. You read that *a rickety wardrobe took up so much room the bedroom door couldn't fully open* (see lines 45–47).

34. **(4, 3, 1, 2).**

    This is a **fact-finding type of question**. The answer is a fact in the text. By reading the text carefully you will identify the correct order of events. Michael looked at: 1. the view of the bridge, 2. the kitchen sink, 3. the fireplace, and 4. the spare room.

35. **It was awkward to turn around.**

    This is an **inferring type of question**. To find the answer you have to 'read between the lines'. You read that the room *on the right was hardly any larger than a cubby-hole* (see lines 35–36) and it *contained a desk, a chair and a wooden cabinet* (see lines 38–39). For a cubby-hole size room it would be very crowded. It could be less awkward in the cramped space to back out than turn around.

READING TEST 4 (pp. 86–94)

1. **both found in northern Australia.**

    This is a **fact-finding type of question**. The answer is a fact in the text. You read that *There are two types of crocodiles in Australia: the freshwater crocodile and the saltwater crocodile. Both are found in the tropical north* (see lines 1–4).

2. **make obvious the size of a crocodile compared to a person.**

    This is an **inferring type of question**. To find the answer you have to 'read between the lines'. Above a line showing length in metres, you see the size of both a crocodile and a person. This indicates that the writer is trying to show a comparison of sizes.

3. **speed at which it can catch its prey.**

This is an **inferring type of question**. To find the answer you have to 'read between the lines'. You read that *Crocodiles can reach speeds of 17 kph over short distances before they tire* (**see lines 33–34**) and that crocodiles strike *suddenly* (**see line 23**). You also read they can cover *12 metres in less than a second—long enough to capture prey before it can react* (**see lines 37–38**). Combining this information you can work out that of the options given, the fact that crocodiles can move very quickly to catch their prey is the most amazing feature.

4. **jaws.**

This is a **fact-finding type of question**. The answer is a fact in the text. You read that *Animals are crushed by the crocodile's jaw pressure, or drowned. It can drag a fully-grown buffalo into the water* (**see lines 24–26**).

5. **lurks.**

This is a **language type of question**. To find the answer you have to read the text carefully. You read that a crocodile *usually waits patiently for its prey to get close to the water's edge before striking suddenly* (**see lines 21–23**). Combine this information with your own knowledge of the meaning of *lurks* which is 'waiting in a concealed position' to work out that *lurks* is the best word to describe how a crocodile catches its prey.

6. **at the water's edge.**

This is a **fact-finding type of question**. The answer is a fact in the text. You read that the crocodile *waits patiently for its prey to get close to the water's edge before striking suddenly* (**see lines 21–23**) then *grabs onto the animal and rolls powerfully. This throws any struggling animal off balance, making it easier to drag it into the water* (**see lines 28–31**).

7. **They are larger than any other Australian animal.**

This is a **fact-finding type of question**. The answer is a fact in the text. You read that *It [the crocodile] is Australia's largest animal* (**see lines 11–12**).

8. **newspaper.**

This is a **fact-finding type of question**. The answer is a fact in the text. You read that you are told to *Start with a full sheet of newspaper* (**see Step 1**).

9. **folding.**

This is a **fact-finding type of question**. The answer is a fact in the text. You have to look at all the pictures. You will see that folding is the main skill required in making a paper hat.

10. **six.**

This is a **fact-finding type of question**. The answer is a fact in the text. At Step 6 you are told to *Stop here for a pirate's hat*.

11. **as a cry of success.**

This is a **language type of question**. To find the answer you have to read the text carefully, especially Step 10: *Bingo! Bingo* is an expression called out when someone has had success, especially in a game of Bingo.

12. **a game with pretend characters.**

This is an **inferring type of question**. To find the answer you have to 'read between the lines'. You read that (Step 1) the hat is made from newspaper. Newspaper is not really practical for a hat in a real situation. It is a play hat. As it can be made into a pirate's hat it would be best for games where children are pretending to be characters.

13. **to the bathroom.**

This is a **fact-finding type of question**. The answer is a fact in the text. You read that *it was a long way across the kitchen. It was even further to the bathroom* (**see lines 3–5**).

14. **the first day at school.**

This is a **fact-finding type of question**. The answer is a fact in the text. You read that *I was scared the day I started school* (**see line 14**). *Scared* means almost the same as *frightened*.

15. **curious.**

This is an **inferring type of question**. To find the answer you have to 'read between the lines'. You read that the narrator wondered about a number of things: *I wondered what was over the other side. Did the world go on forever?* (**see lines 24–26**) and *Some nights I go and look at the stars in the black sky* (**see lines 37–38**). The narrator has an interest in things he doesn't fully understand. He is curious.

16. **a recount.**

This is a **synthesis type of question**. To find the answer you have to read the whole text. The text is about what happens as a child gets older.

Recounts relate a series of events in the general order in which they happen. This passage is a recount.

17. how we see the world as we get older.

This is a **judgement type of question**. You read that the narrator's impression of distance changes as he becomes older. At first it's a *long way across the kitchen* (see lines 3–4). Then the street was *long … go on forever* (see lines 11–13) and finally the Earth *is just a tiny speck in a universe* (see line 43). His impression of size also changes. When he was a baby *Mum and Dad were very big* (see line 1). *In Grade Two I am really big* (see line 27). The text is mainly about how we see the world as we get older.

18. (1, 3, 2, 4).

This is a **fact-finding type of question**. The answer is a fact in the text. By reading the text carefully you will identify the correct order of events: 1. crawling to the bathroom, 2. going to the shops, 3. walking to school, 4. looking at the night-time sky.

19. It's a big world.

This is a **synthesis type of question**. To find the answer you have to read the whole text. The text is about how the narrator's view of the world changes from when he *was a baby* (see lines 1–2) to when he was in grade 2 (see line 27) at school. He describes everything as large. You read *Did the world go on forever?* (see lines 25–26) You then combine these ideas to come up with a suitable title: *It's a big world*.

20. has a vivid imagination.

This is an **inferring type of question**. To find the answer you have to 'read between the lines'. You read that the narrator has never seen the witch but has only heard her as *she scratches her fingernails on the pane / Of the window next to my bed* (see lines 11–13) and *She calls them to come with a 'Who? Who? Who?'* (see lines 5–6). You know this is the sound owls make, and a *lonely owl* may leave feathers behind. There is no witch, except in the narrator's imagination.

21. already prepared.

This is a **language type of question**. To find the answer you have to read the text carefully, especially the section that is quoted: *To come to the feast she's spread* (see line 4). Combine this with your own knowledge of the meaning of *spread* in the context of meals, which is 'laid out or prepared meal'. In this context the poet is talking about a feast that has been already prepared.

22. a tree branch scraping across the glass.

This is an **inferring type of question**. To find the answer you have to 'read between the lines'. You read that the imaginary witch *scratches her fingernails on the pane / Of the window next to my bed* (see lines 11–13). There are trees nearby. You read there is a *tree outside* (see line 1) and the narrator can hear *leaves [rustle] in the trees* (see line 10). Combine this with your own knowledge of noises in the night and you will know it is not a witch scraping the glass but a tree branch scraping the window pane.

23. is feeling scared.

This is an **inferring type of question**. To find the answer you have to 'read between the lines'. You read that the imaginary witch *scratches her fingernails on the pane* (see lines 11–12) so the narrator pulls *the doona with all my might … over my head* (see lines 14–15). Combine this with your own knowledge that children often hide under blankets when they are frightened to work out that the child pulled the doona over her head because she was scared.

24. it sounds like the call of a lonely owl.

This is a **language type of question**. To find the answer you have to read the text carefully, especially the section that is quoted: *She calls them to come with a 'Who? Who? Who?'* (see lines 5–6). Combine this information with your own knowledge that the hooting sound made by an owl (hoo) and the word *Who* are homonyms (words that sound the same which are spelled differently). So the narrator thinks the owl's hoot is a witch's call.

25. real-life work experience.

This is an **inferring type of question**. To find the answer you have to 'read between the lines'. You read *See how a station really works. Join in the daily working life with station staff* (see lines 9–10). Many of the activities available at Beltana, such as mustering and shearing, are work done at the station.

26. feeding lambs.

This is a **fact-finding type of question**. The answer is a fact in the text. You read *For the* *kids … there will be animals to feed—chooks, lambs, calves and alpacas* (see lines 15–17).

27. **encourages people to do artistic things.**

This is a **language type of question**. To find the answer you have to read the text carefully, especially the section that is quoted: *The station is an outback inspiration for painters and photographers* (see lines 18–19). An *inspiration* is something that stimulates the human mind to be creative. Painting and photographing the landscape are artistic activities.

28. **one driver follows a leader in another car.**

This is a **language type of question**. To find the answer you have to read the text carefully, especially the section that is quoted: *self-drive or tag-along trips can be organised* (see lines 24–25). *Tag* has several meanings. In this context it means 'following someone closely'.

29. **learn some Australian history.**

This is a **fact-finding type of question**. The answer is a fact in the text. You read that the station is described as *historic* (see line 7) and *Accommodation includes: The historic 1860s shearers' quarters* (see lines 26–27). This implies that people with an interest in history would be fascinated.

30. **It is called a holiday with a real difference because it is a working holiday.**

This is an **inferring type of question**. To find the answer you have to 'read between the lines'. You read that Beltana Station *is a great place for a holiday with a real difference* (see lines 3–4) and *it covers over 2000 square hectares and is a fully working sheep and cattle station* (see lines 1–3). You also read *Beltana Station is not a resort hotel. Come to Beltana and experience real life with real people* (see lines 32–34). From this information you can work out that the real-life working holiday aspect is what makes Beltana a holiday with a real difference.

31. **the soldiers who guarded the Norfolk Island prisoners.**

This is a **fact-finding type of question**. The answer is a fact in the text. You read that *The soldiers brought rabbits, pigs and goats to the island* (see lines 21–22). The prisoners had *soldiers as guards* (see line 7).

32. **dedicated.**

This is an **inferring type of question**. To find the answer you have to 'read between the lines'. You read that *a slow reclamation has taken place. Work can only be done when the seas are not rough … Once on the island, volunteers have a steep climb up to the worksites* (see lines 35–40). You also read that this work began in 1983 *when it was decided to restore it to its original condition* (see lines 31–32). It has been a long and difficult ongoing job. Combine this information with your knowledge that if you are dedicated you persevere despite hard work and conditions. The people who now visit Phillip Island have to be dedicated.

33. **Phillip Island was not a suitable place for convicts.**

This is a **judgement type of question**. You have to work out which options are facts—that is, information reported as true—and which option is an opinion, which means 'what some people may think or believe'. The statement that Phillip Island was not a suitable place for convicts depends on a person's opinion.

34. **hopeful.**

This is a **judgement type of question**. You read that *The island was neglected until 1983 when it was decided to restore it to its original condition* (see lines 30–32) and *Since then a slow reclamation has taken place* (see line 35). For volunteers to persist with the reclamation for so long under difficult conditions suggests strongly that they are hopeful of success.

35. **arduous and rewarding.**

This is an **inferring type of question**. To find the answer you have to 'read between the lines'. You read that *Work can only be done when the seas are not rough as the island can only be reached by sea* (see lines 36–38) and *volunteers have a steep climb up to the worksites* (see lines 39–40). Combine this information with your knowledge that *arduous* means 'difficult', for you to work out that participants would find the project arduous. You also read that *real progress is being made* (see lines 40–41) so you can work out that volunteers would also find the project rewarding.

ANSWERS TO LANGUAGE CONVENTIONS TESTS

LANGUAGE CONVENTIONS TEST 1 (pp. 96–102)

1. **replied.** *Reply* ends with a consonant and *y*. To add the suffix *ed* you must change the *y* to an *i* before adding *ed*.

2. **swooping.** *Swoop* ends with a vowel and *p*. You simply add the suffix *ing*.

3. **delayed.** *Delay* ends with a vowel and *y*. You simply add the suffix *ed*. Don't get confused with *laid* which sounds the same as (de)-*layed*.

4. **referee.** This can be a tricky word. *Referee* is *refer* + *ee*. The double *ee* on many words refers to a particular activity or occupation (e.g. *trustee*, *employee*).

5. **central.** *Central* is *centre* + *al*. Drop the *e* before adding the suffix *al*.

6. **quarters.** For almost all words containing *q*, a *u* follows the *q*. *Quarter* ends with a single consonant. Simply add an *s* to make the plural.

7. **spine.** Make sure you pronounce the word carefully.

8. **debt.** This is a tricky word. Remember: it has a silent *b*.

9. **professors.** There is no *ff* in **professors**. The *pro* is actually a prefix.

10. **merrily.** *Merrily* is *merry* + *ly*. When a word ends in a consonant and *y* you change the *y* to an *i* and then add *ly*.

11. **switches.** One *switch* → two *switches*. To make plural a word that ends in *ch* you add *es*. If you say the word, you can hear the *es* sound.

12. **phone.** *ph* in *phone* has an *f* sound.

13. **external.** Remember to pronounce the ending as *al* not *le*.

14. **piece.** *Peace* and *piece* are homonyms: words that sound the same which are spelled differently. *Piece* refers to a small bit of something.

15. **keypad.** *Keypad* is a compound word. It is *key* + *pad*.

16. **casing.** When adding *ing* to a word that ends with a consonant and *e*, you drop the *e* before adding the *ing*.

17. **there.** *There* and *Their* are homonyms: words that sound the same which are spelled differently. *There* refers to a place or position.

18. **ground.** The letter combinations *ow* and *ou* can make the same sound. *Ground* belongs to a family of similar words (e.g. *sound, found*).

19. **once.** *Once* is a common word. It is one of those words that simply has to be learned.

20. **along.** *Along* is *a + long*, **not** *all + long*.

21. **female.** *Male* and *mail* are homonyms: words that sound the same which are spelled differently. *Male* refers to men and *female* refers to women.

22. **balance.** Think of the word in two parts: *bal + ance*.

23. **thankful.** The suffix *ful* is always spelled with a single *l*.

24. **advice.** *Advice* is a noun. *Advise*, which has a slightly different pronunciation, is a verb.

25. **celery.** *Celery* is a common vegetable. It is one of those words whose spelling simply has to be learned.

26. **flew.** *Fly* is an irregular verb. Most verbs in English form their past tense by adding *ed* (e.g. *he looked*). There are a number of irregular verbs where this doesn't happen. So *flew* is the past tense of *fly,* not *flyed*.

27. **is.** Subjects and verbs must agree with one another in number. If a subject is singular (*price*, **not** *jeans*), its verb must also be singular (*is*); if a subject is plural, its verb must be plural.

28. **4WDs.** No apostrophe is required. There is no sense of ownership, and *4WD* is an abbreviation for a 4-wheel drive vehicle. The *s* indicates there is more than one.

29. **but.** *But* is a conjunction that joins two ideas in the sentence.

30. **o'clock.** The term *o'clock* is a shortened term for *of the clock*. The apostrophe indicates that letters have been omitted.

31. **on.** *On* is a preposition used to describe something in a position above, but still in contact with, a surface.

32. **Why do you put sugar in your tea?** A question usually requires an answer.

33. **Whether.** *Whether* (*... or*) is a conjunction pair used to indicate alternatives and implies an element of doubt.

34. **flock's.** Even though there are many birds there is only one flock so the apostrophe goes before the *s*. *Flock* is a collective noun.

35. **but there was no call from our visitors.** *But* is a conjunction joining two clauses, the second of which provides additional information.

36. **movie. What.** Bryan makes a statement followed by a question. There are two separate ideas included in what he said. The speech marks (" and ") are not required in the middle of quoted words.

37. **is.** Subjects and verbs must agree with one another in number. If a subject is singular (*billiards* is singular even though it ends with an *s*), its verb must also be singular (*is*); if a subject is plural, its verb must be plural.

38. **HMAS.** There are no full stops for an abbreviation using capital letters. *HMAS* is used for Australian naval ships and stands for: *Her (His) Majesty's Australian Ship.*

39. **Anya said, "What do we do with the leftover food?"** The question mark is included with the actual words spoken. The comma indicates a pause and goes directly after *said*.

40. **brother.** The word *brother* is a common noun. The pronoun *I* is always written as a capital letter.

41. **cleverly, almost, soon, wildly.** Adverbs tell how, when, where and to what extent things are done.

42. **which.** *Which* is a pronoun. It introduces a clause providing additional information about the film.

43. **Pam's.** *Pam* with an apostrophe *s* indicates that the pens belonged to Pam. *Hers* is a possessive pronoun and does not require an apostrophe.

44. **bananas.** The plural verb *grow* goes with the plural subject *bananas*.

45. **toe.** *Toe* rhymes with *grow*. Make sure you use the correct spelling.

46. **eyes,** The line ends with *eyes* and a comma. A comma indicates a pause.

47. **your.** *Your* is a possessive pronoun. It shows ownership. *You're* is a shortened word for *you are*.

48. **Workers at the General Post Office (GPO) are striking for higher wages. Officials at the GPO were not prepared for the strike.** Brackets are used for abbreviations to provide an opportunity to use the shortened term later in the passage.

49. **looking for food scraps.** This phrase refers to *the dogs* which is the subject of the sentence.

50. **big, old, Australian.** There are no strict rules about the order of adjectives but there are conventions most people follow. This one begins with an observable feature, then an age feature, and finally a qualifier.

LANGUAGE CONVENTIONS TEST 2 (pp. 105–111)

1. **shearer.** *Shearer* is *shear* with the suffix *er*. Make sure you have the vowels in the correct order.

2. **forever.** *Forever* is a compound word: *for* + *ever*. *Fore, four* (4) and *for* are homonyms: words that sound the same which are spelled differently.

3. **florist.** The *ist* ending on many words refers to a type of person (e.g. *racist*). The *est* ending is used to refer to the forming of the highest degree of most adjectives and adverbs of one or two syllables (e.g. *best, fastest*).

4. **matron.** *Matron* does not have a double *t* (*tt*). Make sure you pronounce the word carefully.

5. **mayor.** *Mayor* and *mare* are homonyms: words that sound the same which are spelled differently. A *mare* is a female horse.

6. **cherries.** One *cherry* → two *cherries*. When a word ends with consonant and *y* you change the *y* to *i* and add *es* to make the plural.

7. **tidied.** When a word ends with a consonant and *y*, you change the *y* to *i* before adding the suffix *ed* to make the past tense of the word.

8. **citrus.** In many words *c* and *s* have the same sound (e.g. *city, silly*).

9. **plumber.** *Plumber* has a silent *b*.

10. **gliding.** When a word ends with a consonant and *e*, you drop the *e* before adding the suffix *ing*: *glide* → *gliding*.

11. **theme.** *Theme* is a word often used at school. It is one of those words that simply must be learned.

12. **window.** Make sure you pronounce the word correctly. It is *window*, not 'wind**er**'.

13. **curtain.** The letter combinations **er** and **ur** can make the same sound (e.g. *curtain, certain*). Remember when to correctly use each one.

14. **pane.** *Pane* and *pain* are homonyms: words that sound the same which are spelled differently. A *pain* is an unpleasant feeling that hurts.

15. **frame.** The letter combinations **ame** and **aim** can make the same sound. Remember when to correctly use each one.

16. **distant.** Make sure you pronounce the word correctly. It is *distant*, not *distent*.

17. **section.** Take care not to be confused about the correct use of **ct** and **ck** in words. **tion** often has a **shun** sound.

18. **often.** *Often* is pronounced 'offen'. The **t** is silent.

19. **many.** *Many* is one of those common words that simply must be learned.

20. **between.** *Between* is *be + tween*. Make sure you pronounce the word correctly.

21. **waiter.** The correct word is *waiter*, not *water*. A person who waits on a table at a cafe is a *waiter*.

22. **naughty.** The word for 0 (sometimes called zero) is *nought*. *Nought* is not part of *naughty*.

23. **highchairs.** *Highchairs* is a compound word: *high + chairs*. Do not use the shortened form of *high* (*hi*). The letter combinations **air** and **are** can sound the same but are spelled differently (e.g. *fair, fare*).

24. **mystery.** Make sure you pronounce each syllable of the word: *mys + ter + y*.

25. **typing.** When a word ends with a consonant and *e*, you drop the *e* before adding the suffix **ing**: *type → typing*.

26. **you've.** *You've* is a contraction of *you have*. The apostrophe indicates that letters (**ha**) have been omitted.

27. **go.** Subjects and verbs must agree with one another in number. If a subject is singular, its verb must also be singular; if a subject is plural (*Bill and Joe*), its verb must be plural (*go*).

28. **bought.** *Buy* is an irregular verb. Most verbs in English form their past tense by adding **ed** (e.g. *he looked*). There are a number of irregular verbs when this doesn't happen. So *bought* is the past tense of *buy*, not *buyed*. With *bought* you need a 'helper'—another verb to 'help' it. *Has* can be a helping verb.

29. **Ms Ghan said to me, "Time to stop writing."** Only the actual words spoken are in speech marks (quotation marks). A comma follows *me*, indicating a pause.

30. **Islanders** *Islanders* is a proper noun and requires a capital letter. No comma should follow.

31. **white and black** Adjectives in a series are separated by a comma except between the last two adjectives when *and* may be used.

32. **a.** The indefinite article *a* is used before words beginning with a consonant sound.

33. **flag's.** The design belongs to the flag. There is only one particular flag being referred to so *flag* is singular and takes an apostrophe *s* (*'s*).

34. **Oh, is that the time?** A question usually expects an answer. After the interjection (*Oh*) the question really begins with *is*.

35. **Mt** *Mt* is short for *Mount*. As the final letter (*t*) is in the abbreviation, a full stop is not required.

36. **is not.** *Ain't* is not acceptable in formal speech or writing. In this case it stands for *is not* or *isn't*.

37. **aunt's.** There is only one *aunt*. To show ownership an apostrophe *s* (*'s*) is added.

38. **above, between, during, off.** Prepositions show the relationship of a noun to another word in a sentence. They often give the position in time or place.

39. **several, tall, basketball.** There are no strict rules about the order of adjectives but there are conventions most people follow. This one begins with an observable feature, then a description and finally a qualifier.

40. **tries.** *Olivia* is a single subject and must have a singular verb (*tries*). The apostrophe is not required as there is no suggestion of an abbreviation or of ownership.

41. **are.** Subjects and verbs must agree with one another in number. If a subject is singular, its verb must also be singular; if a subject is plural (*police*), its verb must be plural (*are*).

42. **but – also.** *But … also* is a paired conjunction used to indicate one action following a similar action.

43. **who's.** *Who's* is a shortened word for *who is*. The apostrophe indicates that a letter (*i*) has been left out.

44. **among.** *Among* is a preposition used when more than two people are involved. *Between* is used when just two people are involved.

45. **If you look over there, you will see the red bull, the brown cows and the small calves.** Commas are used to indicate a pause after *there*. Commas also separate items in a series (*the red bull, the brown cows*).

46. **How you did it, I will never know.** This is a two-part statement. A question is not being asked.

47. **bubbled.** *Bubbled* is a verb. It is what the creek does: it bubbles along. *Trickling* and *sparkling* are adjectives in this sentence.

48. **silliest.** *Silliest* is a comparative adjective. It is used when comparing more than two ideas. The word *most* is unnecessary as it implies the same idea. *More* is only used when comparing two ideas.

49. **The sugar glider (*petaurus brevicepos*) is a small possum that has the ability to glide from tree to tree.** The scientific titles for common names of animals are written in italics within brackets.

50. **The boys in the house across the street play cards nightly.** *Nightly* means 'every night'. *The*, the definite article, implies *all*.

LANGUAGE CONVENTIONS
TEST 3 (pp. 114–120)

1. **coloured.** *Color* is the American spelling which is not standard in Australia.

2. **bullies.** One *bully* → two *bullies*. When a word ends with consonant and *y*, you change the *y* to *i* and add *es* to make the plural.

3. **claws.** *Claw* ends with a single vowel and a consonant. You simply add an *s* to make the plural.

4. **exclamation.** *Exclaim* is spelled with an *i* but in *exclamation* the *i* is dropped. Its spelling simply has to be learned.

5. **purple.** *Er* and *ur* often make the same sound. It is important to remember when each is used.

6. **catches.** One *catch* → two *catches*. To make a plural of a word that ends in *ch*, you add *es*. If you say the word, you can hear the *es* sound.

7. **scent.** *Cent, sent* and *scent* are homonyms: words that sound the same which are spelled differently. *Scent* has to do with smell. *Scent* has a silent *c*.

8. **mechanic.** This can be a tricky word as *machine* is spelled with an *a*. There is no *k* at the end of the word.

9. **digital.** *Digital* is *digit + al*. *Al* is a common ending for adjectives (e.g. *global, herbal*).

10. **field.** Remember: as a general rule, it is *i* before *e* except after a *c* sound. Remember also: there are quite a few exceptions to this rule.

11. **inform.** *Inform* is *in + form*. Make sure you pronounce the word carefully.

12. **features.** The *tures* ending often makes a *chers* sound.

13. **combed.** *Combed* is *comb* with the suffix *ed*. The *b* is silent.

14. **forehead.** *Forehead* is a compound word: *fore + head*. Take care with the pronunciation of this word. It is not pronounced as it is spelled. *Forehead* is pronounced like *foreign* except it ends with a *d* sound and *foreign* ends with an *n* sound. *Fore* carries the meaning of being at the front (e.g. *foreword*).

15. **bridge.** *Dge* is a common letter combination. Learn the group of words that have this combination (e.g. *ridge, ledge*).

16. **cheek.** *Ee* and *ea* make the same sound in many words (e.g. *see, sea*). It is important to remember when each is used.

17. **balloons.** *Balloons* has a double *l* (*ll*) and double *o* (*oo*).

18. **jokingly.** *Jokingly* is made up of three syllables: *joke + ing + ly*. *Joke* ends with a consonant and *e*. When adding the suffix *ing*, you must drop the *e*.

19. **always.** *Always* does not have a double *l* (*ll*).

20. **your.** *Your* and *yore* are homonyms: words that sound the same which are spelled differently. *Yore* refers to times past.

21. **careful**. The suffix ***ful*** is always spelled with a single *l*.

22. **very.** *Very* and *vary* sound almost the same. Take care with their pronunciation. *Vary* means 'change something'.

23. **debated.** The letter combinations ***ate*** and ***ait*** can make the same sound. It is important to remember when each is used.

24. **condemn.** *Condemn* has a silent *n*, as does *column*.

25. **buried.** *Berry* and *bury* are homonyms: words that sound the same which are spelled differently. A *berry* is a fruit. *Bury* ends with a consonant and *y*. Change the *y* to *i* before adding the suffix ***ed.***

26. **you.** *You* is a personal pronoun and can be both singular and plural.

27. **Irish.** *Irish* is a proper adjective. All other options are common nouns.

28. **The teacher asked if any child felt sick.** This is an example of indirect speech. No speech marks (" and ") are required as the actual words spoken are not given. Questions included in indirect speech do not require a question mark

29. **to.** *To* is a preposition indicating a position. Certain prepositions tend to go with particular situations. They have to be learned and remembered.

30. **km** Mathematical abbreviations do not have full stops. They rarely include capital letters.

31. **world's.** There is only one world being referred to, so *world* is singular and takes an apostrophe *s* (***'s***).

32. **Great Barrier Reef.** The *Great Barrier Reef* is the full name of the reef. It is a proper noun and requires capital letters at the beginning of each word.

33. **over.** *Over* is a preposition indicating a position above a certain point.

34. **I let my dog, Flossy, have a run along the beach.** Two commas are required to separate the dog's name, which is additional unnecessary information, from the rest of the sentence.

35. **was.** Subjects and verbs must agree with one another in number. If a subject is singular (*ten dollars* is treated as a single amount), its verb must also be singular (*was*); if a subject is plural, its verb must be plural.

36. **rang.** Most verbs in English form their past tense by adding ***ed*** (e.g. *he looked*). There are a number of irregular verbs when this doesn't happen. So *rang* is the past tense of *ring*, not *ringed.*

37. **we'll.** *We'll* is a contraction for *we will*. The apostrophe indicates that letters (***wi***) have been left out.

38. **than.** *Than* can be used as a conjunction to introduce a comparison.

39. **more cheerful.** With most multisyllabic words you do not add ***er*** or ***est*** to show comparison. *More* is a comparative adjective. It is used when comparing two people: *the sisters*. The word *most* is only used when comparing more than two people.

40. ***Livistonia eastonii.*** Scientific names for common names are usually enclosed in brackets. Scientific names are often written in italics.

41. **four, big, red.** There are no strict rules about the order of adjectives but there are conventions most people follow. This one begins with an observable number, then a description of size and finally a colour.

42. **They've made a mistake in my exam paper!** *They've* is a contraction for *they have*. The apostrophe indicates that letters (***ha***) have been left out. The other options do not have contractions. *Yours* does not require an apostrophe.

43. **early.** *Early* adds meaning to the verb *left*.

44. **Rotten fruit, smelly bread and squashed cans littered the supermarket car park.** Commas are used to separate items in a list. There is no comma between the last two items if they are joined by *and*. Take care not to be distracted by the adjectives describing the nouns.

45. **against.** *Against* is a preposition suggesting leaning and touching or resting. Certain prepositions normally go with certain verbs.

46. **but, nor, while, although.** Conjunctions are words that join together two single words or a group of words.

47. **them.** *Them* is a pronoun used to relate to a group of people. Its purpose is to remove the need to repeat words or phrases.

48. **Friday,"** The spoken words are broken by *said Paula,* which breaks a complete sentence at *Friday.* The first word after *said Paula* is *and.* The comma indicates a pause. The comma is inside the speech marks (**,"**).

49. **RTA.** Initials for organisations are in brackets after the first reference has been made to the name in full.

50. **while on patrol by the river.** This phrase refers to the *policewoman* who it is describing. The other options relate more to the *dog* and would be out of place if they followed the word *policewoman.*

LANGUAGE CONVENTIONS TEST 4 (pp. 123–129)

1. **studying.** *Studying* is *study + ing.*

2. **welcome.** This is a two-syllable word. ***Wel*** does not have a double *l (ll).*

3. **waste.** *Waist* and *waste* are homonyms: words that sound the same which are spelled differently. The *waist* is that part of the human body below the chest.

4. **signing.** *Sign* has a silent *g.* The suffix ***ing*** is added without any letter changes.

5. **pitiful.** *Pitiful* is *pity + ful.* When a word ends with a consonant and *y,* you change the *y* to *i* before adding the suffix ***ful.*** Remember: ***ful*** as a suffix has only one *l.*

6. **taught.** *Taught* is a tricky word. It is one of those words that simply has to be learned.

7. **avenue.** *Avenue* has three syllables. Take care with the final two letters.

8. **noisy.** *Noisy* is *noise + y.* When a word ends with consonant + *e,* you drop the *e* before adding the suffix *y.*

9. **relaxes.** The letters *ck* can make the same sound as an *x.* It is important to remember when to use them correctly.

10. **equally.** *Equally* is *equal + ly.* It has a double *l (ll).*

11. **compare.** The letter combinations *air* and *are* can have the same sound (e.g. *fair, fare*). It is important to remember when to use them correctly.

12. **steamer.** The letter combinations *eem* and *eam* can have the same sound (e.g. *teem, team*). It is important to remember when to use them correctly.

13. **funnel.** *Funnel* has a double *n (nn)* and a single *l.* Most two-syllable words that end with *l* have just the one *l* (e.g. *travel, oval*).

14. **wheel.** The letter combinations *eel* and *eal* can have the same sound (e.g. *steel, steal*). It is important to remember when to use them correctly. *Wheel* has a silent *h.* *Wheal* (sometimes *weal*) refers to a scar.

15. **deck.** The letters *ck* can make the same sound as *k.* It is important to remember when to use them correctly.

16. **calm.** *Calm* has a silent *l.*

17. **through.** *Through* and *threw* are homonyms: words that sound the same which are spelled differently. *Threw* is the past tense of *throw.*

18. **busier.** *Busier* is *busy + er.* When a word ends with a consonant and *y,* you change the *y* to *i* before adding the suffix *er.*

19. **beginning.** This is a tricky word. Take care with the double *n (nn).*

20. **further.** Make sure you pronounce the word carefully. *Farther* has more to do with distance. *Further* has more to do with amounts.

21. **splashes.** One *splash* → two *splashes.* Add *es* to make plural a word that ends in *sh.* If you say the word you can hear the *es* sound.

22. **turkeys.** One *turkey* → two *turkeys.* When a word ends with a vowel and *y,* you simply add an *s* to make the plural.

23. **listen.** *Listen* has a silent *t.*

24. **nursery.** It is easy to confuse *ur* and *er* in words. It is one of those words that has to be learned.

25. **bonuses.** *Bonus* is a less common word. It is spelled as it sounds: *bo + nus.* Add *es* to make plural a word that ends in *s.*

26. **leave.** Subjects and verbs must agree with one another in number. If a subject is singular, its verb must also be singular; if a subject is plural (*photos*), its verb must be plural (*leave*).

27. **factory.** *Factory* is a common noun and does not require a capital letter.

28. **until.** *Until* is a conjunction indicating up to a certain time but not afterwards.

29. **Miss** *Miss* is not an abbreviation and does not require a full stop. It is an official title and should have a capital letter.

30. **I.** *I* is a personal pronoun which takes the place of the name of the person speaking.

31. **Tracy, you are always a welcome visitor.** A comma follows *Tracy,* indicating a pause. It separates the person spoken to from the rest of the sentence.

32. **from.** *From* is correct. The use of *off* is a common speech error. Remember *off* is the opposite of *on.*

33. **Capt.** If a title is shortened but still retains its last letter, no full stop is required. The *t* in *Captain* is not the last letter so a full stop is required.

34. **am not.** *Ain't* is not acceptable in formal speech or writing. In this case it means *am not.*

35. **The first day of spring is a Thursday, which was named after Thor, the god of thunder.** Only *Thursday* and *Thor* are proper nouns. Sentences always start with capital letters.

36. **GST.** Initials for official terms are in brackets after the first reference has been made to the term in full.

37. **ski, was, thought, believe.** Verbs can express an action (*ski*), a state of being (*was*) or a feeling (*believe*).

38. **beautiful, old, pink.** There are no strict rules about the order of adjectives but there are conventions most people follow. This one begins with an observation, then a description of age and finally a colour.

39. **more capable.** With most multisyllabic words, *er* or *est* are not added to show comparison. *More* is a comparative adjective. It is used when comparing two people (the boys). The word *most* is only used when comparing more than two people.

40. **me?** This is a question the narrator is silently asking herself.

41. **lunchtime,"** *Lunchtime* is the last word spoken. It is followed by a comma for a pause and then the speech marks are closed.

42. **couldn't.** *Couldn't* is the contraction of *could not.* The apostrophe indicates that a letter (*o*) has been omitted.

43. **after school."** *After school* is the last spoken word in the sentence. It concludes with a full stop inside the speech marks.

44. **without moving his lips.** *Silently* and *without moving his lips* carry the same meaning. The option *without moving his lips* is redundant, i.e. it isn't needed.

45. **You are in time for a meal, but have you eaten, Jenny?** The first comma comes after *meal*. It indicates a pause. The second comma is used to make the meaning clear. (We hope no-one is intending to eat Jenny!)

46. **work.** Subjects and verbs must agree with one another in number. If a subject is singular, its verb must also be singular; if a subject is plural (*electrician and his apprentice*— two people), its verb must be plural (*work*).

47. **"Is.** The first word of direct speech has a capital letter. It comes after the speech mark (").

48. **had been wound.** This is a past participle. *Wound* is an irregular verb. Most verbs in English form their past tense by adding *ed* (e.g. *he looked*). There are a number of irregular verbs where this doesn't happen. So *wound* is the past tense of *wind,* not *winded.* With *wound* you need 'helpers'—other verbs to 'help' it. *Had* and *been* can be helping verbs.

49. **A bright, green, flashing light was seen during the eclipse.** Commas separate adjectives in a series. There is no comma between the final adjective (*flashing*) and the noun (*light*).

50. **any.** The options of *none* or *nothing*, along with *don't,* are examples of double negatives which are incorrect. *Any* is used to indicate a part or fraction of something.

Notes

Notes